George a [handwritten]

Nutt Uncut

Thanks for all [handwritten]

David Nutt

your help [handwritten]

Foreword Ilana B Crome

Best wishes David [handwritten signature]

 WATERSIDE PRESS

Nutt Uncut
David Nutt

ISBN 978-1-909976-85-6 (Paperback)

Cover design © 2020 Waterside Press by www.gibgob.com. From an image that first appeared on the cover of *The Week* now owned by the author.

Distribution Drug Science: drugscience.org.uk

Cataloguing In-Publication Data A catalogue record for this book can be obtained from the British Library.

Printed by Severn, Gloucester, UK.

Published 2020 by
Waterside Press Ltd
Sherfield Gables
Sherfield on Loddon, Hook
Hampshire RG27 0JG.

Telephone +44(0)1256 882250
Online catalogue WatersidePress.co.uk
Email enquiries@watersidepress.co.uk

All proceeds from the sale of this book go to Drug Science.

Table of Contents

Publisher's note

The views and opinions in this book are those of the author and not necessarily shared by the publisher. Readers should draw their own conclusions concerning the possibility of alternative views, accounts, descriptions or explanations.

Acknowledgements

I have been extremely fortunate to have been supported by many exceptional people throughout my life. Without them things would have been very different. Special thanks must go to my wife Di, and our four children, Jonathan, Stephen, Suzannah and Lydia, who have been both my fiercest critics and greatest supporters. I am especially grateful to my parents and, as I was the first child of my generation, my aunts and uncles were always hugely positive about almost everything I did. As a child I was truly in receipt of a surfeit of the uncritical positive regard so vital for developing children's sense of their own worth. Mr Gregory my junior schoolteacher, who introduced me to science, needs a special mention, and we stayed friends for decades after I had left his school.

My research career wouldn't have happened if not for the opening given to me by David Grahame-Smith at the Medical Research Council (MRC) Clinical Pharmacology Unit. And, particular thanks are due to his deputy, Richard Green who supervised my thesis and put up with my arrogance and occasional rudeness with remarkable patience. Michael Gelder the Professor of Psychiatry at Oxford facilitated fast-tracking my clinical psychiatry training to allow me more time for research which then resulted in me obtaining my Wellcome Trust Senior Clinical Fellowship. My two-year spell at the National Institutes of Health (NIH) in the United States of America (US) was made possible by Markku Linnoila and Boris Tabakoff, who headed the Alcohol Institute there. I am especially grateful to John Lewis, the Head of Research for Reckitt and Colman for funding me to return from the US to set up my own Psychopharmacology Unit at Bristol University in 1988. I would also like to thank Professors Jimmy Mitchell and Gethin Morgan for welcoming me to their university.

Also, thanks are due to the Edmond J Safra charity who funded my professorship at Imperial College London. My charity Drug Science would not have existed without the vision and financial support of Toby Jackson, plus Richard

Garside who hosted us at the Centre for Crime and Justice Studies at King's College London.

Finally, I want to thank all those who worked with me as colleagues and students and without whom I would have achieved nothing. Many I have mentioned in the text and the students are listed at the end of *Chapter 16*.

It is important to mention that this book doesn't cover all my research and clinical work, just topics and events that I felt are most interesting to the general reader. So, there are some colleagues and research themes that I have left out despite their having played a huge part in my career. Specifically, I would like to mention Alan Hudson and Robin Tyacke for their pioneering work on imidazoline receptors and their ligands, and Anne Lingford-Hughes for her leadership of our addiction imaging research team that included Jan Melichar, Fergus Law, Mark Daglish, Louise Paterson, Liam Nestor and Judy Myles.

David Nutt
October 2020

About the author

David Nutt is the founder of Drug Science and Chair of its Scientific Committee. He is the Edmund J Safra Professor of Neuropsychopharmacology and Head of the Neuropsychopharmacology Unit in the Centre for Academic Psychiatry in the Division of Brain Sciences, Department of Medicine, Hammersmith Hospital, Imperial College London.

He is also Visiting Professor at the Open University and Maastricht University in The Netherlands. His leadership positions include (or have included) the presidencies of the European Brain Council, British Neuroscience Association, British Association of Psychopharmacology and the European College of Neuropsychopharmacology, as well as Chair of the UK's Advisory Council on the Misuse of Drugs. He is a Fellow of the Royal Colleges of Physicians, Psychiatrists and the Academy of Medical Sciences; UK Director of the European Certificate and Masters in Affective Disorders courses; and a member of the International Centre for Science in Drug Policy.

David Nutt has edited the *Journal of Psychopharmacology* for over 25 years and acts as the psychiatry drugs advisor to the British National Formulary. He has published over 500 original research papers and a similar number of reviews and book chapters, eight government reports on drugs and 31 books, including *Drugs Without the Hot Air*, which won the Transmission Book Prize in 2014 for Communication of Ideas. His full CV appears in the *Timeline* at the end of *Chapter 16* of this book.

The author of the Foreword

Ilana B Crome is Professor Emerita of Addiction Psychiatry at Keele University. She is Chair of the Board of Trustees of Drug Science; Honorary Consultant Psychiatrist, Midlands Partnership NHS Foundation Trust, St George's Hospital, Stafford, Staffordshire; and Honorary Professor, St George's University of London.

To all three generations of my family for their total and uncritical support and for putting up with my many irritating traits and behaviours.

Nutt Uncut

Foreword

Ilana B Crome

I was thrilled to read the autobiography of Professor David Nutt. He once told me: 'I just love my job!'. This is reflected in the sheer enthusiasm with which he recounts an in-depth picture of his professional and personal journey: the choices he made, the outcomes achieved, and their nuanced interrelationships.

Looking back, very early on, David Nutt already displayed many of the characteristics which propelled him along the trajectory he depicts. Even as a young child, as his values were forming, he was troubled by injustice and inequality. At the same time he questioned and was inspired by teachers and peers. A prestigious scholarship to Cambridge set him on the route to discovery and achievement which culminated in accolades throughout his career. As he progressed through clinical medical and psychiatric training in the most esteemed centres in the UK and abroad, he continuously availed himself of opportunities to extend his scientific understanding in the neurosciences, especially psychopharmacology, as he sensed that these fields were about to flourish.

His energy resonates throughout: he is clearly passionate, excited and optimistic about his ongoing academic work, which is in full swing. While he is serious, he sees the humorous side of situations and is fun; he can be daring and direct; he is without a hint of arrogance. He is always ready to listen, examine, assess and re-assess. He is keen to support, encourage and provide opportunity.

Highly accessible anecdotes and vignettes bring the book to life, demonstrating Professor Nutt's warm, caring and humane nature, and intense concern for those in distress. His objective is to alleviate people's anguish, whether by kind and careful clinical intervention, by generating novel research questions, or by driving wider policy or political change. Not only has he been prolific but he has sought to tackle some of the UK's most pressing social and medical issues. He has made a vital and lasting contribution to problems that affect us all. By assimilating his vast knowledge of clinical medicine and psychiatry, and psychopharmacology, and by delving deep into the evolution of drugs policy, he has brought to the fore the necessity for an informed public and scientific debate around the fears, contradictions and complexities of designing drug policy. This is the story of that path.

However, this is not just the story of one person. It is also the story of the evolution of modern medicine, psychiatry, and psychopharmacology in the UK and internationally. It is about the social history of the medical profession and scientific community, it is about the wider ramifications (including unintended consequences) of health policy, it is about the political scene. It is about the courage and conviction to question the evidence on which treatment, scientific findings and policy-decisions are based.

This book is a modest, honest, and vibrant portrayal of an exceptional contribution to these developments. No figure in public life has integrated medical, psychiatric and scientific expertise with well honed public communication skills more successfully than Professor David Nutt. Little did I know when I first met him 50 years ago, as we were beginning our medical training in Cambridge, that we would pursue broadly similar careers. Our enduring association has culminated in collaboration at Drug Science, the mission of which is to advance addiction research, and to appraise evidence to influence the uppermost echelons of medical policy-making.

This is a book I just could not put down! I was captivated, and I guarantee that you have a treat in store.

October 2020

'There is a tide in the affairs of men which taken at the flood leads on to fortune'

Brutus—William Shakespeare, *Julius Caesar*

'David Nutt has been a towering intellectual figure in drug policy for 30 years, and has revealed the absence of an evidence base for global drug policy. He will continue to be a central influence on drug policy, making this book a must read for all who are interested in that debate.'

Baroness Molly Meacher

CHAPTER 1

Becoming Conscious: Politics and the Science of Breathing

I have always had a fascination for understanding how the world works. In infant school I can remember arguing with a girl in my class against the existence of God because there had to be someone or thing to have made him. I can identify my love of science beginning in 1959 when at junior school my form teacher, Mr Gregory, conducted the collapsing can experiment. He took an empty gallon petrol can, added about half a pint of water, and then put it on a tripod with a Bunsen burner underneath. The cap was off so we could see the steam escape as the water boiled. Then he screwed the lid on tight and turned off the burner. We all waited suspiciously. Was anything going to happen — why should it? Then without warning the can collapsed in on itself with a loud bang that shook us all up. What force could have done this he asked? Of course, we had no idea about atmospheric pressure until he told us that this had collapsed the can; as the steam cooled and condensed back into water this reduced the pressure in the can below that of the outside air, and at some point the pressure differential collapsed the can.

Further proof of this strange concept of atmospheric pressure came with the next experiment. Mr Gregory put a piece of thin flat cardboard over the top of a glass that was nearly full of water. He then turned it over quickly, so the opening was now facing down. The class watched expecting the water to fall to the floor, but to our collective amazement the water stayed in the glass even though it was upside down.

From that point I realised I had to accept that one's own sense of the world couldn't tell us everything. One could never feel atmospheric pressure because it's inside us as well as outside of the body; experiments were the only way to properly identify the 'facts' of the real world.

But the real world at that time had some unscientific and unpleasant facts. The Cold War was at its height, a nuclear Armageddon was always on the cards and we had regular and to me quite disturbing tests of air-raid sirens in case the Russian rockets were launched against us. In Africa, the first Congo revolution had broken out with the children caught in the middle starving to death. I found the images of skeletal children with their stomachs bloated by kwashiorkor profoundly distressing and offensive to my sense of humanity and justice. So aged eleven I got permission from my headmistress to collect unwanted items from the local population and run a 'jumble sale' to support the Save the Children fund. I am not sure it made much if any difference to the Congolese children but the value of doing something active to challenge injustice has stayed with me ever since.

Following passing my eleven plus exam I went to Bristol Grammar School (BGS), the leading grammar in the city where I continued to do well in most subjects and get more skilled at science. In hindsight the science facilities and teaching were outstanding, close to what universities offer today. I loved chemistry and in the chemistry club spent a few weeks making (1) chloro (3) bromo (5) iodo-benzene just to see if I could. It turned out to be a rather uninteresting brown oily liquid. By then (1967) the Summer of Love was in full flow and LSD had become a major factor in the immense social artistic and music revolution of which this was part. I suggested the chemistry club might do a demonstration synthesis for the next Open Day for parents but was advised to stick to a molecular model instead.

As well as chemistry, biology was my other star subject. My skills at dissecting the earthworm meant I was given that task for the Open Days. I would stand over the specimen and describe the internal organs to any parent with stomach enough to look over my bench and into its innards.

I also had a reputation for being a bit challenging to staff which led to a memorable interchange between the senior French teacher and my father at a parents evening.

My dad: 'So how is my son's French?'
Teacher: 'Well he will never make ambassador in Paris.'
Dad: 'Oh, is his French that bad?'
Teacher: 'No, his French is OK, but his diplomatic skills are non-existent!'

Luckily, I had by then already decided that the Foreign Office was never going to be a career ambition.

One of the great strengths of BGS were the weekly sixth form lectures given by external speakers. Two had significant impacts on my career. The first was a psychotherapist whose name I have long forgotten, but his talk about the nature of interpersonal relationships and the complexities of developmental conflicts and attitudes made a lot of sense of the behaviours I was seeing in my friends and their families. It also made the study of psychological processes seem not only interesting but tractable.

The other was by a Professor William Grey-Walter, a true genius in terms of fusing engineering with medicine. He was one of the pioneers of recording brain waves using the electroencephalogram (EEG), and showed us how you could from reading these detect that people were planning to say something before they even knew they were: the first, if primitive, example of mind-reading. His work was conducted in an MRC unit at the Burden Neurological Unit just on the outskirts of Bristol and he invited a few of us to visit and see the new EEG and other technology on which he was working. One of these was brain evoked potentials, a technique for estimating alterations in brain function that he developed to help in the diagnosis of multiple sclerosis. At that point I knew I wanted to have my own brain research unit.

Grey-Walter's book — *The Living Brain* (1963, W W Norton) — became my first in-depth contact with brain science. It's still worth reading today, as he was so ahead of his time as a thinker about the brain. Perhaps his most famous invention was the Turtle — the first autonomous robot. It would wander around the lab avoiding walls and obstacles and then, when its battery was running down, it would plug itself into a wall power socket to recharge. All this before the invention of microchips and computers. Sadly, his career was ended when he suffered severe brain injury following a motorcycle accident. As well as impairing his memory and attention, the brain trauma, because it damaged the frontal parts of his brain, also profoundly changed his personality so ruining both his personal and work relationships. It is testimony to his love of excitement that, despite knowing how vulnerable brains are to trauma and how dangerous motorcycling was as a pastime, Grey-Walter couldn't curb his own drives and energy and stop doing it. Clearly the intellectual brain is sometimes, maybe never, able to control desires and urges, even in the most knowledgeable brain experts.

My interest in medicine came later, and rather accidentally. I had decided to apply to study Natural Sciences at Cambridge University with a view to developing a research career as a human physiologist or psychologist. I decided to try for Cambridge because at that time (1968) it had the most Noble Prize winners in the world. Walking into the entrance to the biochemistry building at 17 and seeing displays of the discoveries of Perutz, Sanger and Crick with their structural models of haemoglobin and DNA was inspiring.

Getting into Cambridge at that time involved an entrance exam taken the term after A-levels. These exams were surprisingly interesting as they made you think rather than regurgitate knowledge. One of the questions remains with me 50 years later—estimate the number of molecules of air from Socrates last breath each of us take in every time we breath! Getting the answer is easy as all you need to estimate is the volume of air on the earth, the volume of Socrates last breath and your current lung volume, and the number of molecules of oxygen and nitrogen in a litre of air. Of course, there are assumptions like an even distribution of molecules from the last breath in the atmosphere, but given that was over 2,000 years ago that seems reasonable. What's the answer you may ask? It's about five molecules. But it's not the result that really matters—it's how you think about solving the problem that counts.

I was called up to interview in December 1968 but the day before that I accidentally opened the rather large University Prospectus at the Medical Sciences section. Glancing through I realised that it was identical to the Natural Sciences one with the exception that anatomy replaced zoology. It then came to me that learning human brain anatomy might be more relevant to my career ambition than studying the zoology of amoebae. In the long run being a doctor might be the more practical way forward when I wanted to study humans rather than other species. Till then I hadn't ever thought of being a doctor—I was always set on being a scientist—but began to realise that being both might be the best way to achieve my ambitions.

So, the next day at interview when the senior tutor said to me, 'Nutt, so you have come for an interview to do Natural Sciences?' I replied that I had changed my mind and wanted to do Medical Sciences instead. Consternation spread across his face. New interviewers were hastily sought so I could be grilled by the Medical Sciences tutors as well.

That afternoon I had what must be a record of six entrance interviews but obviously managed to impress some of them enough to be allowed in to study Medical Sciences.

Umbilical research

At that time the Oxbridge entrance exams took place just before Christmas, which for most of us meant we came back to school for an extra term after the A-level exams. Once these exams were over, we had the rest of the academic year free. In reality, this was the longest holiday of our life—the precursor of the current 'gap' year phenomenon. The plan was generally to get work, save as much money as one could by continuing to live off one's parents and then travel over the summer. Since I always wanted to be a researcher, I approached the Physiology Department at the University of Bristol to see if they had any six months' research assistant posts. They offered two, and I chose to work with Dr Alan Rogers, a solo researcher with an interesting background and a reputation for irascibility. Alan was an unusual researcher being a trained medical doctor who had then returned to the 'bench.' He had made his reputation as a human physiologist and expert on life in extreme conditions having had the unique experience of being the doctor on the 1956–58 Vivian Fuchs expedition to the South Pole, the first trans-Antarctic crossing. Alan had to train as a dentist as well to gain his place on the team and when I joined him he was still analysing some of the physiological records he had taken, to explore the effects of extreme cold on heart rate and blood pressure.

My job was to help him develop methods to measure and then extract the newly discovered hormones called prostaglandins. Alan was interested in the mechanisms that underpin the closure of the blood vessels in the umbilical cord after birth. It's a common fallacy that the cord needs to be tied then cut. In practice, within minutes after the baby is born, the cord vessels clamp shut. It is obvious this must happen since all other mammals then chew through their cords without any ligature to stop bleeding. The big challenge for us was to get the vessels to open up again so we could explore the role in prostaglandins shutting them down. To do this we had to insert fine glass tubes into either end of one of the tightly contracted arteries (there are two per cord) and try to get a physiological saline solution to pass through them. In most cases they wouldn't reopen, so then we tried the other one. When occasionally one did open, we could measure the pressure it took to pump the saline fluid through them and then measure the changes in pressure produced by adding prostaglandins to the fluid. Alan preferred to measure the pressure changes the traditional way with a needle tracing out the pressure wave-form on a revolving smoked drum (a kymograph) whereas I liked to use the new-fangled oscilloscope that the lab had just purchased. Simple, in principle at least, but where to get the cords? The nearest maternity hospital was several miles away so I had to get the bus there carrying a jar of freshly made up saline solution, make my way to the maternity suites where if I was lucky I might have three cords waiting for me, which I then transported back on the next bus. The cords were skin-white with jelly oozing out of each end and the odd fleck of blood clot at the ends of the arteries, like some extra-terrestrial worms. I clutched the jar tightly all the way desperate to avoid a spillage.

The highlight of my six months research experience was the lambing season when Alan had access to a number of pregnant ewes on which we would operate to allow us to measure umbilical blood flow, pH and oxygen saturation before and after (caesarean) delivery. He was interested in how circulation in the cord changed from when the baby was inside to outside the uterus. In particular, he had the idea that full oxygenation that would happen when the baby lamb started to breath might be the stimulus to the umbilical arteries shutting down. As you might imagine this was a major operation, just like human caesarean sections are, with full anaesthesia and ventilation of the mother. Each operation lasted all day and well into the evening as we had lots of equipment to prepare and calibrate before the operation started. Each operation was tiring, challenging and needed fluent teamwork, so good practice for my time as a medical student and house surgeon.

We also attempted to measure prostaglandins in the cords which involved grinding them up in a blender and extracting the organic matter in ethyl acetate. This was then shaken up with chloroform which was supposed to capture the prostaglandins. The chloroform solution was then dropped onto one end of a large glass chromatography plate that was coated with a silica paste and the plate was then dipped into an ethanol solution, which shifted the prostaglandins along the plate as it rose up by surface tension. The plates were then dried and different sections were tested for prostaglandin activity using a bio-assay of gerbil intestine. This—a classic gut-bath experiment—involved a piece of intestine being strung up between a tension meter (force transducer) and a fixed hook. If a part of the silica plate had prostaglandins present then the gut would contract, with the force produced directly related to the amount of prostaglandins that were there. At that time the chemical structure of prostaglandins hadn't been identified so we were right at the beginning of the field and quite in the dark as to whether we were succeeding. Now we understand much more about them and their role in many body processes. We even use a synthetic prostaglandin to help induce labour by dilating the uterine cervix; and others we give as medicines to protect the stomach from ulcers. I left Alan and Bristol University in July 1969 grateful for my first experience of hands-on research with no idea that 20 years later I would be back in the same building running my own research group.

Pre-clinical medicine in Cambridge

In the October of 1969 I 'went up' to Downing College, Cambridge—for three interesting and rather eventful years. The first night set the tone as the nine Medical Science undergrads in the college gathered together (as doctors tend to do) to get to know each other in the pub. Downing was, like all Cambridge colleges at the time, a single sex college so we were all males which probably explains why we went to the pub. At that time the college closed its gates at 10.30 pm and to stay out longer required signed permission beforehand from your tutor, often several days before. Mindful of this we trouped back at 10.29 pm just as the pub was closing and continued to drink wine and whisky in college. About two hours later one of the group who had been tanking it back more than most started to cry out in a wailing, tearful voice. He was so sad and despairing that I thought he had become suddenly severely depressed and might be suicidal. One or two of the more alcohol-experienced others reassured me that it was just the alcohol talking so we didn't call the ambulance service, just put him to bed.

The next day he was fine with no recall of the events of the night before and, even more amazingly no hangover. This episode left an indelible mark on my memory and mind, despite my own not-insignificant alcohol intoxication at the time. How could a drug change someone's personality so profoundly and abruptly? I suspect it was this incident that sowed the seeds of my lifelong interest in psychopharmacology (the study of how drugs affect the brain and mind) and my interest in recreational drugs and addiction.

I was soon to discover that I too could experience alcohol-induced tearfulness. On the night of the Garden House 'riot' I was a protestor in the grounds of the hotel, where a dinner to encourage travel to Greece was taking place. Parts of the student body had blockaded the travel agents in the city earlier in the day in protest against their tacit support for the military junta's takeover of Greece. We had just seen the film *Z* which exposed their evil tactics and many students felt strongly — like Lord Byron had a century before — that the seat of democracy should not be a military dictatorship. Though I felt strongly about Greece the hotel protest worried me, especially once I found myself squeezed up against a policeman of my own age whose back was against a large glass window behind which were the diners. The prospect of the glass caving in and cutting us to shreds seemed imminent so I retreated back to a social (i.e. drinks session) at a gathering of the college badminton team.

There, perhaps because of the heady influence of a day of protests, I got very, very drunk on wine (at the time a new drink for me as we hadn't had it at home). I was so intoxicated that I couldn't stand and remember crawling on my hands and legs across the college lawn. This was quite against the rules as only 'college fellows' were allowed in the sacred grass! But it was a more direct route and the paths were gravel, so painful on the hands and knees! Eventually (the Downing lawn is huge) I made it to my staircase, up the one flight of stairs and to the door of my room. But I couldn't work out which key to use and as I was trying each of them unsuccessfully the key ring broke and they all fell to the floor around me (I was sitting too drunk to stand). This disaster made me break down in tears and my wailing brought the fellow who lived on the staircase also to my aid. He located the key, opened the door and put me to bed.

Next morning I woke with a pounding headache and a wet feeling over my chest and my mattress and I slowly realised that I had vomited in the night. This insight terrified me as I knew the dangers of vomiting in sleep — it had only recently killed Jimmy Hendrix. As I hastily cleaned up the mess before our 'scout' (Cambridge undergrad slang for the daily cleaner) arrived. I realised how lucky I had been to have fallen asleep face down. From then on I took a more circumspect and safety-first approach to heavy drinking, even though I was drunk many more times. I also made sure that my friends and my children's friends were put into the recovery position when drunk.

The Garden House protest had significant repercussions for a number of my peers. Sometime after I had retreated, the hotel windows did break and protestors fell inside. Because the Riot Act had been read out (for the first time in many years in the UK) the police were given special powers to arrest these protesters and the courts punished them severely. A judge famous for being especially hardline (exemplified by his house being called Truncheons), was appointed to oversee the review and punishments. Several students of my college were sent down (dismissed from the university) and one went to a young offender institution despite being the grandson as a Sea Lord. Being quite different in background and education to the others there he found it quite difficult and when he returned a year later was a broken person, without his previous energy and commitment to change. That episode should have taught me that the Establishment wasn't going to take challenges lightly, but I continued to push for change and two years later my college was under siege by students, but more of that later.

My first knowledge of (un)consciousness

At that time teaching us how to conduct and analyse our own experiments was at the centre of medical sciences teaching and in physiology and psychology we were sometimes our own subjects. One I remember clearly was to explore how our brain responds to low levels of oxygen. Most of us have experienced gasping for breath and feeling aroused and even anxiety when pushing exercise to the limit. Could this reflect a lack of oxygen or was it due to excess carbon-dioxide build up? Most of us—and probably most of you reading this—assumed it was low levels of oxygen that made us gasp for breath. So we were amazed to find out this was not the case.

It's a simple experiment, you just breath air from a closed bag through a face mask. But the outflow air passes through a pipe and into a solution of sodium hydroxide. This is alkaline and carbon-dioxide is acidic so they chemically react to put the carbon-dioxide into solution as a carbonate salt. This way the carbon-dioxide levels in the inspired (i.e. breathed in) air in the bag never rise though the oxygen concentration falls as it is used up in the body. To test changes in brain function we began writing sentences whilst breathing from the bag. For about 20 seconds nothing happened then we found ourselves being woken up by the supervisor as we had, without any warning, crashed into unconsciousness. Looking back, we saw our writing begin to disintegrate about a second before this. The loss of consciousness occurred without any warning; there was no anxiety or breathlessness. It was silent and unnoticed and would have been lethal had not someone intervened and taken the mask off.

Apparently, health and safety concerns preclude this form of experimentation today which is a shame because those few seconds of sudden un-warned loss of consciousness carry a vital message—the human brain cannot detect low levels of oxygen. Why this should be so is unknown, probably reflecting the rarity of ever breathing air low in oxygen and low in carbon-dioxide in the pre-industrial world. But this insensitivity to oxygen explains several aspects of life—and death—today. The most obvious example is the safety information on aeroplanes in relation to a loss of pressure. This always directs parents to put their own oxygen masks on first, before putting one on a child. This reflects the reality that when oxygen concentration falls a parent could lose consciousness without warning if they spend time helping children. The children might then survive but wouldn't be able to rescue the parents by putting masks on them.

Covid 19 has presented the medical profession with many challenges but one of the most puzzling has been those patients who die because they stop breathing without any sense of breathlessness. If caught in time their blood oxygen levels can be as low as half what they should be but because their carbon-dioxide levels are normal they don't feel short of breath so don't seek help. Without blood oxygen monitoring their doctors don't know they are hypoxic.

Psychiatrists are more aware than most doctors of this peculiarity of the brain's insensitivity to oxygen. Those, like me, who work with heroin addicts see this all the time in our patients who often stop breathing for a minute or more after taking an intravenous (IV) shot of this opioid. They stop breathing because heroin shuts down that part of the brain which drives the breathing rhythm but the low oxygen doesn't offset this. Those of us who work with patients at risk of suicide are well aware of the risk of deaths from carbon-monoxide poisoning, now involving car exhausts but previously coal gas.

The inability of our brains to detect low levels of oxygen explains why so many people die each year from carbon-monoxide poisoning, either deliberate suicide or accidently in rooms with inadequately ventilated gas heaters. Carbon-monoxide is a gas which is produced by incomplete combustion of carbon as in petrol or propane gas. Carbon-monoxide binds more strongly to haemoglobin in the blood than oxygen so reduces the oxygen carrying capacity of blood which leads to death from hypoxia (low oxygen). The fact that hypoxia does not lead to arousal or anxiety explains why these deaths occur with the victims undisturbed. The loss of consciousness comes on without warning, so the victim, even if awake and contemplating suicide, is unable to change their mind once the effect sets in.

In the 1960s suicide by carbon-monoxide poisoning was relatively common because domestic heating gas was made from coal and contained a lot of carbon-monoxide. Reports of people committing suicide by putting their head inside an unlit gas oven, were particularly common. One happened to be a fellow Cambridge student whilst I was there. Preventing this form of suicide led to one of the greatest ever health interventions, the replacing of coal gas with natural gas that is free of carbon-monoxide. In the ensuing 50 years tens of thousands of deaths from suicide have been prevented.

Carbon-dioxide is the carbon gas with which most people are familiar. It is the product of carbohydrate metabolism in our bodies. Because it's always being produced it needs to be eliminated to prevent it harming the body. So we breath it out. The more carbon-dioxide is made, the faster and deeper we breath to eliminate it. These changes in breathing are driven by the level of carbon-dioxide in the body because it stimulates the brain centres that control breathing (i.e. carbon-dioxide stimulates the brain processes that get rid of it). This means that our brains, like those of all mammals, are exquisitely sensitive to increased carbon-dioxide levels.

You can easily demonstrate this yourself, simply hold your breath for a minute. For most of us that is not possible because the urge to breath becomes overwhelming, and this is driven by the increased carbon-dioxide levels in the blood because we are not breathing it out. If I prevented you from breathing, e.g. by putting a plastic bag over your head, then you would become distressed and frightened and fight to breath, as happens when people are drowning. Carbon-dioxide drives powerful arousal and escape behaviours through activation of the fear centres of the brain so that we literally 'fight for air.'

Most of you might manage 30–40 seconds of breath holding before giving in, but many of my patients with anxiety disorders, particularly those who have panic attacks, can only manage five or ten seconds. For reasons we don't yet fully understand, their brains are especially sensitive to carbon-dioxide. Because of this I (and others) have developed carbon-dioxide inhalation procedures to mimic anxiety in normal healthy controls. This has allowed us to study the brain processes underpinning anxiety in a more systematic way. It has also facilitated the study of how established treatments for anxiety work, and so allowed us to accelerate the development and testing of potential new treatments. This is an example of the experimental medicine approach to mental illness that I have made the backbone of my research over the past 40 years.

Mentors and mistakes

One of the great advantages of Cambridge was the immense wealth of teaching talent. How many people have had the experience of being taught a whole course by a Noble laureate—Alan Hodgkin? He worked out how neurons transmitted information through the passage of electrical potentials across their cell membranes and along their axons. This is still one of the foundation studies in the history of neuroscience which underpins all our understanding of how the billions of cells in the brain communicate. One evening I was invited to the Downing high table and had the pleasure of sitting next to Andrew Huxley (who also got the Nobel Prize with Hodgkin) who was visiting from University College London and spent the meal explaining his new theories on how muscles work and how dolphins could spend so long under water. At that time, I hadn't realised that Aldous Huxley the author of *Brave New World* (his best known work) was his stepbrother, so missed the chance to explore their relationship as half-brothers and their possibly different attitudes to brain science.

Two other influential figures were the Iversens. Les discovered the way in which neurotransmitters such as noradrenaline were recycled through being taken back into the nerves they came from through re-uptake sites. He then showed this was how the frontline anti-depressant drugs at that time such as amitriptyline worked. His wife Sue, in the sixth month of her pregnancy, gave a stellar lecture series on psychopharmacology—how neurotransmitters control brain and behaviour and how drugs work on them. Together they confirmed to me that this was the area of science I wanted to research.

There were two key fundamental theories of brain physiology developing in Cambridge at the time that defined the rest of my career. The first was the concept of allosteric changes in protein function, originally described by Max Perutz for haemoglobin. When oxygen binds to one sub-unit of the haemo-globin protein its shape changes so the other three sub-units can more easily bind more oxygen. This phenomenon was then discovered in many proteins. In the brain it was shown to explain how ion pumps in neuron membranes work to make action potentials and then how drugs alter the shape of proteins to change their function.

The second revolution came in the discovery of chemical transmission in the brain. The concept of neurotransmitters in the peripheral nervous system was long known, e.g. the role of noradrenaline and acetylcholine in control-ling heart rate. But though these were also in the brain they couldn't explain the switching on and off of neurons.

My college tutor was a senior lecturer in physiology—Jimmy Mitchell. He was exploring the role of amino acids such as gamma-aminobutyric acid (GABA) in brain excitability and soon it became clear that in the brain GABA calmed down most neurons (and in the spinal cord it was another amino acid—glycine). But what turned neurons on? Glutamate was suspected but it took many more years to prove this. The same year as I left Cambridge Jimmy did too. He was appointed Professor of Pharmacology at Bristol University and they appointed an Australian chemist, Jeff Watkins, to develop new glutamate analogues. Jeff's work revolutionised our understanding of glutamate receptors and the role off glutamate as the primary excitatory neurotransmitter in the brain. It was now proven that the brain was a chemical, not electrical machine, and the key mediators of its activity were neurotransmitters and the receptors they worked on. Bristol became a world centre for GABA/glutamate research which was one reason I later set up my research centre there.

Although the medicine course was challenging it wasn't all-consuming and I managed to get a 'blue' for badminton (representing Cambridge in the annual blues match against Oxford) as well as, in my last year, becoming the college student president. This student rep role coincided with the student uprisings in many countries, particularly France. Some aspects of their rising spirit of opportunity and rationality spread over many of us in the UK and the Downing students decided to challenge some of the arcane, centuries-old rules of university and college life such as the 10.30 pm curfew. This led me into my first major confrontation with 'the Establishment,' and was one event which didn't go well. Two students were 'sent down' for refusing to comply with college regulations and I led a protest against this that resulted in Downing being laid under siege for a weekend by Cambridge Students' Union.

This student protest was led by a man with whom I would have dealings in the future—a Charles Clarke—who later became Home Secretary in the Labour government. At that time, he was a left-wing student president, memorable for his strong views and a massive head of wavy ginger hair (that he was later to lose) sprawling half-way down his back.

I was fortunate not to be expelled also. I'm sure the college fellows wanted to send me down as well but, because I was a 'scholar,' I was formally answerable to the university rather than the college, so they couldn't. Looking back now I realise how lucky I was to have survived because had I been sent down I would not have graduated and so would probably not have been allowed to complete my medical training, and a research career would have been difficult. Life for me would have been quite different and it's extremely unlikely I would be writing this book now.

But enough of Cambridge. With some relief to escape the student protests I left Cambridge in June 1972. I spent the summer in the US working on building sites in Florida experiencing racism in the real world—the white workers never ate with the black ones—and when I asked why, the response was 'They're different.' Then, with my savings I travelled the whole country largely sleeping on Greyhound buses and getting an ulcer in the process. In October I went to Guy's Hospital in London to study clinical medicine.

Medical training in London and my first psychiatric patients

At that time the University of Cambridge did not have a clinical training course so after three years there all the medical students migrated down to one of the London medical schools to meet their first patients. I went to Guy's Hospital, one of the oldest UK hospitals, just south of London Bridge in Southwark. Although I saw medicine as a necessary stepping-stone to a research career I became remarkably taken by it as a profession and engaged in the learning and practice with more energy and enthusiasm than I had expected. The intellectual challenge of making a diagnosis was stimulating and there was a great deal to learn, and I was good at learning and passing exams.

My interest in the brain and mind meant that for my elective period I chose to go to the local community psychiatric hospital (St Olave's) rather than to wildest Africa like many of my peers. This was an old Victorian workhouse that had been converted into a psychiatric hospital which served the local communities of Southwark and Deptford, so the tough and poor end of the social spectrum with a lot of financial and housing deprivation. Soon after I started with my consultant, Raghu Gaind, a shortage of junior doctors meant that I was asked to take up a locum position and began treating patients for the first time.

I suppose most medics remember their first 'real' patient, the first one for whom they are the primary decision-maker. Mine was a man in his late-20s with schizophrenia. Interviewing him was difficult because his sentences were fragmented and didn't make sense. Also, he kept saying he could smell fish and this smell had a significance for him, as it told him that people were out to get him. His diagnosis was therefore one of paranoid schizophrenia—his paranoia was indicated by his sense that people were out to harm him though he couldn't give any real reasons why this was the case, or why he should be targeted. These kinds of paranoid symptoms are quite common and one of the cardinal features of a diagnosis of schizophrenia.

The fish smell is far less usual. Altered perceptions are often seen in schizophrenia; they are usually related to hearing sounds or voices that aren't there. Smells are quite rare and may reflect a different cause. The most common illness associated with a sense of altered smell is a form of epilepsy called temporal lobe epilepsy. The epileptic fits in this form of epilepsy emerge from a region of local (focal) damage to the temporal lobe of the brain. The temporal lobes are the lower lobes, one on each side just behind the eyes, and the nerves which detect smell go straight into them. When the focus of epilepsy begins to get activated in the build-up to the generation of a seizure this neuronal (nerve cell) activity spreads to the smell centres, so inducing a sense of smell. This often acts as a warning to the patient with the epilepsy that a seizure is imminent, and they can take action to avoid the onset of a fit.

Strangely sometimes this takes the form of using a stronger smell to suppress the epilepsy. Just as increased activity in the epileptic focus can change activity in the smell centre so increased activity in the smell centres can in some cases reduce the activity in the epilepsy focus. Strong smells such as camphor or lemon (e.g. smelling salts) have for centuries been used to alter consciousness and these can suppress some cases of temporal lobe seizures. Even more remarkably it appears that in some people their brain can learn to mimic the smell suppression of epilepsy. After a number of episodes of using the smell some patients can then suppress their seizures just by remembering the smell.

The fish smell that my first patient complained of might have indicated that the temporal lobe was involved in his schizophrenia. There is clear evidence that this might have been the case as alterations in temporal lobe size and function have been reported in many people with this disorder. Also, people with temporal lobe epilepsy have an increased likelihood of developing psychotic symptoms such as paranoia and disorders such as schizophrenia. I questioned my patient to decide if he had ever had a seizure, even as a child, for if he had then I might have treated him with an anti-epilepsy (anti-convulsant) medication. Many children have fits when they have a high temperature (these are called febrile seizures) and there is a genetic basis to these. Generally, they leave no residual impact but in some cases when the febrile seizure is prolonged for more than 20 minutes it can lead to damage to a temporal lobe that can in turn lead to epilepsy and impulsive behavioural disorders when they are adult.

The treatment of paranoia usually requires the use of anti-psychotic medicine that blocks the action of the neurotransmitter dopamine. Neurotransmitters are chemicals that nerves use to communicate between one another. There are at least 80 different neurotransmitters known and maybe still some to be discovered, but dopamine was the first to be identified and one that is now known to be important in a range of psychiatric disorders. In fact the first drug that truly worked to alter the course of a psychiatric disorder was one that turned out to block dopamine activity in the brain—chlorpromazine. This drug revolutionised psychiatry and medicine because it was the first effective treatment of schizophrenia, the most damaging and costly of all psychiatric disorders.

Until the discovery of chlorpromazine there was no effective treatment of schizophrenia so the number of patients hospitalised with this lifelong illness increased year-on-year to a peak in 1952. Since then this number has fallen year-on-year because chlorpromazine and its descendants produce sufficient clinical improvements in patients to allow them to go home and be treated in the community. But the discovery of chlorpromazine was pure serendipity. Two French psychiatrists, Jean Delay and Pierre Deniker, were exploring a range of new sedative medicines in different psychiatric disorders. Having tested promazine and found it sedating and sleep-promoting they then tried a new chlorinated derivative chlorpromazine. This too was sedating but had an unexpected and novel action to reduce psychotic symptoms. To celebrate and explain this radical new discovery they coined the term neuroleptic (brain-calming) drug for chlorpromazine.

Chlorpromazine was a serendipitous discovery so in the early-1950s there was no science to explain its actions, but this changed a few years later when dopamine was discovered as a neurotransmitter in the brain. Several pharmacologists such as Arvid Carlsson in Sweden and Paul Janssen in Belgium discovered that dopamine activity was enhanced by stimulant drugs such as amphetamine and that chlorpromazine acted to dampen down or block this enhanced activity.

Once dopamine and the action of stimulants had been discovered this gave pharmaceutical companies a means to discover new dopamine blockers. They could give rats amphetamine to make them hyperactive, and then test a range of drugs till they found ones that blocked the enhanced activity. In this way a new set of chlorpromazine-like compounds were found, medicines such as haloperidol, fluphenazine and trifluperazine. It was the last of these that I used to treat my patient with the fish smell and paranoia. It certainly helped his paranoia though the smell persisted, but to a lesser extent, and it seemed to cause him less distress.

It wasn't for a further few years that the real pharmacological explanation for the action of chlorpromazine was revealed and this required the discovery of the concept of receptors. These are proteins that are the target of neurotransmitters and which mediate their activity. In 1974 the dopamine receptor was discovered as the target for all known antipsychotic drugs by Phil Seeman in Canada using radioactively-labelled binding techniques. This then led to another phase of antipsychotic drug discovery when receptor binding assays rather than animal studies were used to make new dopamine blockers. This new binding technology also opened-up the new world of receptor-based drug discovery that has delivered many of the drugs we use today.

Now we have a range of different drugs for psychosis that all work to block the over-activity of dopamine that we believe to be the cause of many cases of schizophrenia. These differ in terms of their activity at other receptors so have quite different adverse effect profiles. This means that they can appear as very different drugs: some such as olanzapine and quetiapine cause a lot of sedation and weight gain whereas others such as amisulpride and pimozide have a quite different profile causing more muscle stiffness and endocrine problems. Modern psychiatrists have to choose ones whose side effect profile best suits their patients.

That six weeks elective locum position immersed me in patients with a range of different psychoses. Some had beliefs of possession and influence and others were just pestered by a continuous stream of 'other people's' voices in their ears, the so-called 'third person auditory hallucinations.' These voices are of other people saying things like 'He's going to the shops' or 'What an idiot he is today.' Sometimes if there is more than one voice they can even conduct a conversation between themselves, sharing negative opinions about the patient. This is obviously hugely distressing to the patient. These 'third person' voices are one of the diagnostic features of schizophrenia. They may be the voice of someone known to the patient or just a generic person or persons. Third person voices are rarely if ever experienced in other psychiatric disorders. Voices are heard in other disorders especially severe depression, but then they tend to be in the second person. Common contents of depressive voices are phrases like 'You're worthless,' 'You're a failure' which can be considered internal verbalisations of the persistent self-critical thinking that depressed people get locked into.

The nature of verbal hallucinations has recently been clarified by the work of Chris Frith and his team using fMRI imaging. It seems that when we speak or even plan to say something the part of the brain that puts the words and sentences into place suppresses the part of the brain that we use to understand words that come in through our ears. They presume this is to prevent us getting confused and believing our own intended speech is coming from outside. This internal suppression system breaks down in people with psychosis, so they do appear to hear their own planned speech as being from outside of themselves and so from others. We can see why people with depression hear their negative thoughts as voices but why people with schizophrenia hear voices from other people is still a mystery. It may reflect a breakdown of the sense of self-versus-others that can happen in this disorder and lead to other psychotic experiences such as others being able to read their thoughts or even that their thoughts are being broadcast outside of their heads.

I decided then to study psychiatry. The remarkable multitude of ways in which the brain can go awry in psychiatric disorders was so much more interesting and challenging than the impact of disorders of other organ systems. Additionally it raised questions on the nature of consciousness and the role that upbringing and environment play in the development of the person.

CHAPTER 2

Shocking Times: Bombs and Life Threats

The bomb went off at midnight. My latest recruit, Alan Hudson, was asleep in the Bristol University visitors' hotel and was woken by a huge blast that blew out a floor of the Senate House building just across the road. It turned out that the anti-vivisectionists had planted about a pound of high-quality plastic explosives behind a radiator in the refectory floor of the building. They proclaimed the next day that this was done because Bristol University had welcomed the vivisectionist David Nutt into its ranks. This university had long been a target for the anti-vivisectionist extremists. It appears I had provoked them by doing an interview with the local newspaper explaining how I was planning to research anxiety disorders and addiction using, amongst other things, animal models.

Luckily, they had set the timer wrong. They had planned to blow-up the building at lunchtime when it would have been full of staff having their lunch. But unlike the IRA, from whom it turned out they had obtained the explosive, they weren't expert concerning timers. They had mistakenly thought that 12.00 pm was 12.00 am so the bomb went off 12 hours too late. In fact, they had warned the police that a bomb was in the building that morning. I had just arrived back from a clinical meeting at the local psychiatric hospital and was stuck in the chaos of the evacuation. The building was cleared and searched over the lunchtime but the bomb was not found because it had been stuffed deep behind a radiator.

This failure didn't deter the anti-vivisectionists. Some months later they bombed the cars of two vets, one a colleague of mine working at Bristol University and one working at the Porton Down research establishment in Wiltshire. The Bristol bomb was placed under his car when it was parked outside the university. It exploded just after it fell off the car as he began to drive home. He was unscathed but a splinter of metal shot across the road and injured a baby in a pushchair. The Porton Down vet was less fortunate as the bomb set her car on fire and she suffered burns.

Because my research was specifically mentioned in relation to the Bristol University bomb, I was put under the protection of the anti-terrorism police. They taught me how to check for bombs under my car each day before going to work. I also had my name changed on the electoral role and my address removed from it. To this day my wife and I still vote under assumed names. Thankfully, my Bristol house and car have so far not been attacked.

The research community lobbied government strongly to make the anti-vivisectionists' behaviours a specific criminal offence. They never did, I believe because some MPs shared more supportive views on animal research. However, things got a lot better when the government brought in anti-terrorism legislation to help deal with the IRA bombing of English cities. This was drafted broadly enough to allow anti-vivisectionist activities to be caught under the same Act, and their ringleaders were sent to prison for long terms. Now some are due for release from prison and we have to hope they no longer support violent protests.

What drives such hatred against researchers? These extremists are the tip of an iceberg of opposition to animal and other research and this came to my own personal crescendo when I moved to Bristol University. But it wasn't the first time I had been targeted. My research career seemed to have been a source of irritation to several groups opposed to its broader purpose and rationale, and not just animal experimentation. It began in 1980 at my first scientific conference, at Leicester University, when I was doing my PhD research at Oxford University. To the amusement of my supervisor Richard Green and my colleague Phil Cowen, I turned up in my best interview suit. Apparently academics dressed down not up when presenting their data, to avoid the claim of being marketeers! But my incorrect dress code was but a minor glitch compared with what came next. As we approached the university building where the conference was being held, we could see a large crowd outside. My first thoughts were 'Wow, I didn't know so many people were researching electroconvulsive therapy (ECT).' This was a special conference dedicated to the efficacy and brain mechanisms of this form of treatment.

But as we got closer it became apparent that these weren't researchers, they were the opposite — anti-researchers. They were mostly supporters of the

Scientology organization who were trying to stop the conference because they believed that ECT didn't work and they had better alternative treatments. They had blockaded the doors and were waving anti-ECT and anti-psychiatry placards. Outnumbered, we retreated and found a back entrance into the building. The conference started despite the hostile chanting from outside.

This turned out not to be the last time my conferences were challenged by Scientology; its adherents often turned up to protest at European and American psychiatry meetings, pursuing their anti-scientific claims that anti-depressants don't work, ECT should be banned, mental illness is just a delusion of the medical profession, etc. One motivation for my writing this book is so I can put into the public domain, in non-specialist terms, the truth about psychiatric disorders and their treatments. It is important we counter these extreme and unfounded claims.

Back in the conference I prepared to give my first ever public scientific presentation. A couple of weeks before I had tried it out on our research team at the MRC Clinical Pharmacology Unit in Oxford where I was doing my research degree. I adopted a contemplative-discursive style of presentation, I thought somewhere between Hamlet and Mark Anthony at their best. When I finished there was no applause, just a stunned silence. Then with his usual blunt manner, Richard Green spoke. 'That was rubbish Nutt... Next time try telling us just what you did, why you did it and what the results were.' 'And cut out all the pseudo-philosophical nonsense.' This turned out to be excellent advice that over the past 35 plus years I have passed down to my many research students.

Richard had one other gem of advice on making scientific presentations. This was that you should always talk in a way that makes things easy for you audience. That way they will understand everything you say and assume that's because they are as clever, if not more so, than you. But I you make it too complicated for them then they will blame you for not making it clear! Since then I have pursued this public speaking strategy, trying to make things seem simple but ensuring I can answer the hard questions when they come.

The conference was the first, and I think perhaps the last, ever dedicated to ECT in the UK. It coincided with a phase of anti-psychiatry, particularly anti-ECT, that from the late-1970s was sweeping the world. A number of countries and some US states had banned ECT in the public sector as being barbaric and non-scientific. The anti-psychiatry movement invigorated by the writings of

Thomas Szasz in his book *The Myth of Mental Illness* (1961, Harper) was in full swing. Italy had just passed the Basaglia law that eventually led to the closure of all public mental hospitals and the banning of ECT in them. Psychiatry was under attack with ECT being the first battleground.

This was the public scene when I came into research in 1979 with Professor David Grahame-Smith in Oxford. I had always wanted to do research and as I said in *Chapter 1* only studied medicine to make it easier for me to do research on the human brain. Though at this time I had only just a couple of years' experience in psychiatry I had plenty of experience of ECT. In those days, the most junior doctors were given the responsibility for running the ECT clinic. Also, it suited me as before coming into psychiatry I had a lot of experience in neurology where epileptic seizures are common and often problematic. I found the concept of medically-induced seizures being beneficial rather than harmful particularly interesting.

Even so at first, like most medical practitioners do, I found ECT a little concerning. As doctors we are taught to be wary of seizures as they can cause brain damage from a lack of oxygen if they go on for too long. But it quickly became clear that this couldn't happen in the clinic because we had an anaesthetist ventilating the patient with oxygen. In addition, ECT seizures were relatively mild, sometimes almost impossible to see, because the patients are given a muscle relaxant before the ECT to prevent excessive muscle spasms. It turned out that the biggest challenge with ECT was not seizures that were too long, but those that were too short. One of the significant discoveries reported at the Leicester conference was that for a good therapeutic outcome each ECT seizure had to last 30 seconds or more. Anything less than that didn't seem to reliably lift mood. We often had to find ways to increase the seizure duration in our patients in order to pass the 30 second threshold.

At first this usually involved stopping any anti-convulsant medicines they were on, especially benzodiazepines for anxiety. Alternatively, we could increase the amount of electricity passed across the head. Later I began to use caffeine to make the brain more susceptible to seizures. Having a fit is a well-recognised adverse effect of drinking too much caffeine in energy drinks such as Red Bull. We would give an intravenous infusion of caffeine just before the ECT to lower the seizure threshold and prolong seizure duration.

ECT as given in the First World was humane, nothing like it is portrayed in the book *One Flew Over the Cuckoo's Nest.* In this novel by Ken Kesey (later a film starring Jack Nicholson) ECT is given without anaesthesia or muscle relaxation as a punishment for bad behaviour. Its opponents try to portray this fictional account as the real world and punishment as this as the real justification for its use. Though this is a ridiculous claim it would clearly be preferable not to have to generate a seizure to achieve the same clinical benefit. Especially because ECT can in some cases lead to impairments of recall of some past memories. Though this effect on specific past memories is relatively rare it can be distressing even though the main effect of ECT on memory is to improve it. The research that ECT improves memory was first presented at the Leicester conference. At first sight the theory seems paradoxical but the explanation is that depression impairs memory so profoundly that as ECT lifts the patient's mood so also their memory improves likewise and this more than offsets any detriment produced by the seizures.

My ambition when starting my research in Oxford was to try to work out how ECT worked in the brain and then invent ways of replicating this. The dream was to test the theory that we could get the efficacy of ECT without having to give people a seizure. There is no doubt in the psychiatric community that ECT is the most powerful anti-depressant treatment we have, often working when all other drug treatments have failed. But it does have such a bad press that many patients and their relatives are fearful of it. The anti-ECT brigade has cultivated a lot of negative press coverage that is compounded by misleading films such as *One Flew Over the Cuckoo's Nest.* So how does ECT work and how can we study what it does in the brain?

Working with depressed humans being given ECT was too difficult because then in the late-1970s we had few tools to directly explore human brain function. So, I decided to model ECT in rodents and then explore whether other types of non-electric seizures might produce similar changes. At that time the prevailing theories of how anti-depressants worked was that they enhanced either serotonin, dopamine or noradrenaline function in the brain, so did ECT also affect one of these neurotransmitters?

Modelling ECT in the rat allowed us to study the effects different numbers of ECT treatments had. Normally a course of ECT in humans runs to eight or 12 seizures given twice a week. The effects on mood come on gradually.

Typically, after the first few seizures some improvement in appetite and interest is seen. These effects may last for a few hours and then gradually, later in the course, after four to six treatments we see increased energy and activity. The last symptom of depression to improve is the sense of self-critical negativity and depressed mood which may take ten or more seizures to lift.

When we began to plot out the time course of the neurotransmitter changes in rats, we found that the dopamine system was enhanced after just a single seizure. The enhancement of the serotonin system was much later in coming, taking at least six seizures to begin to become enhanced. This made sense in terms of what we saw in our patients. Depressed people usually have lost their appetite for food and other drives such as sex. They also complain of a great loss of energy and motivation. All these problems are thought to originate in parts of the brain that dopamine plays a major role in, so a deficiency of dopamine would lead to a loss of these drives and processes. In addition, drugs that deplete (e.g. reserpine) or block dopamine (e.g. neuroleptics) function were known to produce depression in some people. The disorder classically attributed to dopamine deficiency, Parkinson's disease, is also associated with depression and loss of appetite. Moreover, these can be rectified by drugs that replace or augment dopamine function such as L-DOPA, amphetamine or apomorphine.

The test we used to measure dopamine function was L-DOPA given with monoamine oxidase inhibitors (MAOIs) (drugs that prevent the breakdown of dopamine). L-DOPA is an amino-acid that is the precursor to dopamine. Giving dopamine itself doesn't work because it can't cross the blood brain barrier, the membrane that protects the brain from many chemicals and some drugs. L-DOPA does get into the brain and is then converted immediately to dopamine. Its ability to replenish depleted dopamine stores in Parkinson's disease was discovered in the late-1950s and was one of the great breakthroughs in brain science and medicine. The discovery of the fact that Parkinson's disease was due to a deficiency of dopamine and how L-DOPA could be used to rectify this is brilliantly described by Oliver Sacks in his book *Awakenings* (later made into a film of the same name starring Robin Williams and Robert de Niro).

When L-DOPA is given with an MAOI a large build-up of dopamine is produced in the brain that leads to characteristic behaviours such as running (locomotion), rearing and sniffing. These are the same as produced by drugs such as amphetamine that release dopamine. We know that these activities in the rat reflect enhanced dopamine activity as they can be attenuated by drugs that block dopamine receptors. After a course of ECT in rats the activating effect of L-DOPA was greatly enhanced. Our research showed that this enhancement of dopamine function could be seen one day after just a single ECT seizure. This could explain the clinical observations that basic drives such as eating might be restored early in a course of ECT but that the mood changes occurred a lot later.

Over many subsequent years of researching ECT we gradually established that there was a progression of changes in the key mood neurotransmitters. Dopamine was the first to be enhanced, coming on after just a single seizure but growing in effect over the next few. Then from the third ECT enhancement of the noradrenaline system began to kick in. We believe this translates into the clinical observation that depressed patients' drive and energy becomes normalised. They show more interest in life, become more active and begin to engage in their prior activities. However, their mood is still low with negative self-critical thinking that is characteristic of depression, persisting until eventually the serotonin system becomes enhanced — or restored to normal functioning.

This delay in serotonin enhancement presents a serious challenge to the clinical teams looking after depressive patients. Because the increased energy and drive occurs before the mood improves this can allow patients to act out their suicidal thinking. One of my first patients as a junior psychiatrist was a farmer in his twenties who we admitted because he was deeply depressed. He responded well to the first weeks of ECT treatments to the point he seemed well enough to be allowed home on weekend leave to start to rebuild his business. He didn't return as planned on the Sunday evening and the next day we heard he had hanged himself in his barn that evening.

Some patients commit suicide despite being obviously on the road to recovery. This is a well-recognised (though thankfully still pretty rare) experience of those who treat people with depression. We believe this is because when they are in the depths of their depression they just don't have the energy and drive to act out their suicidal ideas, but as ECT begins to work and re-energise them, they become physically and mentally empowered to act on their self-harm intentions. This period of enhanced suicide risk during recovery from depression is also seen with anti-depressant drug treatment and psychotherapy. It's an inevitable consequence of the improving mood and drives.

One of our goals in researching ECT was to discover neurotransmitter changes that it produced that might also be induced by medicines rather than by seizures. The discovery that ECT had a triple action, to enhance dopamine noradrenaline and serotonin function, made others wonder if drugs that enhanced these neurotransmitters might be more effective than the pure or selective re-uptake blockers such as the selective serotonin re-uptake inhibitors (SSRIs). Historically there was a suggestion that this might be true because of the clinical efficacy of the MAOIs such as phenelzine and tranylcypromine. These drugs prevent the breakdown of these three neurotransmitters and clinical experience tells us that they can work in patients where selective anti-depressant drugs have failed. In my clinical practice I would always try one of these in cases of 'resistant' depression before moving on to ECT. And some patients did very well, though often despite some significant adverse effects such as low blood pressure.

The MAOIs are not much used because they suffer from one major problem which is interactions with other medicines, cold cures, and some foodstuffs (e.g. cheese). These can lead to elevations in blood pressure with severe headaches. Though the risks of these interactions are not as great as made out in many textbooks they are real, and so drugs without these risks are preferred. The original tricyclic, amitriptyline, had activity at both noradrenaline and serotonin re-uptake but had major toxicity problems in overdose (see *Chapter 4*). So, could a safer multi-neurotransmitter re-uptake blocker be made? In the end several have been developed with the first being venlafaxine (Effexor). This was discovered by Wyeth and was, as we had predicted, a significant advance in terms of efficacy over the SSRIs. Now venlafaxine is the preferred anti-depressant drug for severe depression especially for those requiring admission to hospital. In high doses it elevates noradrenaline and serotonin function; perhaps at very high doses it has a slight effect on dopamine too.

The search for a triple re-uptake blocker was more difficult, designing molecules to block dopamine as well as serotonin and noradrenaline re-uptake proved challenging. Still eventually several were made but, as yet, none have reached the clinic. The main reason for this is that enhancing dopamine function is quite activating—as anyone who has taken amphetamine or cocaine can testify. One of the first triple re-uptake test compounds kept the volunteers it was first tried on awake all night, despite having been given in the morning! It might be that there is a delicate and precise balance that needs to be achieved between dopamine and the other two neurotransmitters.

The other possibility is that the mechanism by which ECT enhances dopamine isn't mimicked by dopamine re-uptake block. Evidence for this comes from the work of David Heal in our Oxford group who showed that ECT, rather than increase the levels of dopamine, made the dopamine receptors more active. Our work had shown ECT's effect on noradrenaline and serotonin was to increase the production and availability of these neurotransmitters and, if anything, reduced the activity of their receptors. Now there are studies using drugs such a pramipexole that directly target dopamine receptors as possible depression treatments, and these might more closely mimic the actions of ECT.

These academic approaches to understanding ECT to improve and even replace it cut little ice with the anti-vivisectionists. During my time at Oxford I had them come to my home. I was at work, so just our child-carer and one-year-old son were there. They threatened her that if I didn't stop my research right then they would do to our beloved black Labrador Ben what I was doing to the rats in my lab! A few weeks later I received an envelope with a card. On the cover was a single word — Expiation. Innocently I opened it and found it contained a poem dripping with evil intent and threats to me if I carried on my research.

Of course, given my personality such pressures only fuelled my determination, but I know of colleagues who to protect themselves and their family decided to give up live animal research after such threats. And I don't blame them, threats are a horrible experience.

Beyond ECT — Can we replace it?

My main ambition was always to find alternatives to ECT. Perhaps the dual noradrenaline and serotonin re-uptake blocker venlafaxine was one? But maybe there were other approaches? One obvious question was whether the electricity in ECT contributed to the therapeutic effects, or was it just the seizure? As I have observed above the seizure was vital because if it was less than 20 seconds little clinical benefit ensued. Also, there was growing evidence that the electricity contributed to the adverse effects of ECT. Once the threshold level needed to induce a seizure had been reached, the more current that was passed the more problems with memory resulted.

Were there other ways to induce a seizure as an alternative to ECT? History told us that this was indeed the case. Before ECT had emerged in the 1950s therapeutic seizures had been induced by chemicals. Camphor was used in the 1800s but the real breakthrough was the discovery of pentylenetetrazol. In the 1930s this was called an analeptic or arousing agent and used to wake people up from barbiturate comas, usually due to overdose. Then it became used as a means of inducing therapeutic seizures as a treatment for depression. It was widely used and was sold by several different companies under trade names such as Metrazol, Cardiazol and Leptazol. Still in the 1990s it was being used in sub-convulsant doses to magnify epileptic activity in the brain during EEG studies so as to allow the location of the epileptic focus be determined. In *Chapter 3* we will discover how positron emission tomography (PET) imaging has now replaced this for diagnosis.

Like most medicinal treatments in the last century, at the time pentylenetetrazol was discovered we had no idea how it worked. But by the time I started my research it had been identified as a blocker of the GABA receptor. The GABA receptor system had been recently discovered, by amongst other people, Professor Jimmy Mitchell, my tutor at Cambridge. It was soon shown to be the main inhibitory neurotransmitter in the mammalian brain. GABA was responsible for keeping the brain calm, an effect opposed by the excitatory neurotransmitter glutamate. The activity of the brain is determined by the balance between these two neurotransmitters. I like to make the analogy that the brain is always walking a tightrope between too much glutamate and too much GABA. If glutamate dominates then anxiety and seizures occur whereas if GABA dominates then we are asleep or unconscious. All normal brain functioning requires these two neurotransmitters to work in perfect balance, like yin and yang.

To lay down memories we need to increase glutamate activity in the neurons that will encode the memory. To do this we can increase glutamate release, as occurs for example in times of great stress where it can lead to laying down post traumatic stress disorder (PTSD) memories. Or we can decrease GABA release locally at the same time as there is a small increase in glutamate activity in the memory circuit, which is how the brain normally lays down memory.

Drugs that decrease GABA activity can therefore lead to memory formation as well as anxiety and seizures.

It was this GABA blocking effect of pentylenetetrazol that led to its being superseded as a treatment for depression by ECT. On some occasions when patients were given pentylenetetrazol a seizure didn't occur, but the anxiety production and memory encoding effects persisted. The patients remembered vividly the anxiety the drug had produced and were naturally unhappy to have another dose. Many of them ran away from the hospital or clinic to escape further treatments. One reason ECT was adopted so rapidly across the world was because, unlike pentylenetetrazol, it didn't leave traumatic memories. One old colleague of mine who had worked in Poland in the early-1950s recounted how the staff embraced ECT because they no longer had to drag anxious and unwilling patients into the pentylenetetrazol treatment room. Those that had been given ECT were quite happy to walk quietly to their next treatment.

Exploring this history, I discovered there had been no research into the effects of seizures induced by pentylenetetrazol and other GABA blocking drugs such as bicuculline. So I decided to see if they would produce the same changes in brain function as ECT in rodents. If this was the case, then maybe we could use sub-therapeutic (and sub-anxiety producing) doses of GABA blockers to enhance brain function in an anti-depressant direction.

It was already known that repeated sub-convulsant doses (i.e. of convulsants) could lead to enhanced activity, a phenomenon known as 'kindling.' We found that this did occur. Repeated low doses of several different GABA blocking drugs enhanced the effects of dopamine, but sadly not serotonin. So it did seem that ECT had something chemical seizures didn't. A few years later Richard Green clarified the reason, it turned out that one of the key effects of ECT was to enhance GABA function, whereas with pentylenetetrazol we were reducing it. This might be the reason that serotonin function wasn't enhanced. Whatever the reason this line of research didn't develop into the clinic and pentylenetetrazol is now just a footnote in the history of psychiatry and psychopharmacology.

And what of ECT? Since the dark days of the 1970s there has been a fightback from the medical profession and other health experts. ECT is a proven effective treatment that is still available in most countries and health jurisdictions. The technology to deliver electricity to the brain to maximise clinical benefit and minimise adverse effects (especially those on memory) has progressed a lot. The new ECT machines can also measure the EEG to allow more precise determination of the duration of each seizure, so ensuring they are long enough for therapeutic efficacy. If they are too short, then the dose of electricity given in the next treatment is increased a little.

Could ketamine replace ECT?

The role of glutamate in lifting mood has also developed in an unexpected but powerful way with the growing use of ketamine to treat depression. Ketamine is a glutamate receptor antagonist that dampens consciousness to a point where anaesthesia results. This activity explains why ketamine has been used for decades as an anaesthetic agent. It's the only anaesthetic that doesn't depress respiration, so ketamine is popular where there are few, if any, anaesthetists. This includes low income countries so for example over 40 per cent of operations in Zambia are carried out under ketamine. Ketamine is also popular in emergency situations including battlefields, where it is known as the 'buddy drug' because it's so safe that any soldier can give an injection of it to their injured comrades.

Ketamine is really the only glutamate-blocking drug we can safely use in patients. For this reason John Krystal at Yale University started using it to explore glutamate receptor function in the brain. He thought that the psychological dissociation and altered state of consciousness that ketamine produced, when given in sub-anaesthetic doses, might be a useful way to model aspects of schizophrenia in normal healthy subjects (which it is). But during this research he also noted that some of his participants reported improved mood for a day or so after the experiment. It's interesting that this serendipitous observation was replicated in our studies of the psychedelic psilocybin in normal volunteers (described in detail in *Chapter 12*). Some also reported they feel better for days or weeks after having the psilocybin experience despite this being in the claustrophobic environment of the MRI scanner.

In both cases the accidental discovery of improved mood led to a trial of the drug in depression with positive outcomes. Krystal and his team then conducted a trial of ketamine in patients with resistant depression and found a clear beneficial effect. But in contrast to other anti-depressant drugs (though in some ways similar to ECT) the effect was almost immediate. The patients' moods began to improve as they came out of the altered state of dissociation and confusion that the ketamine produced. The next day they were significantly better, but this effect then gradually wore off so by the end of a week they had slipped back into their previous depression.

Since this pilot trial there have been over a dozen replications of the finding that ketamine can help people overcome a depression that has failed to respond — or to adequately respond — to anti-depressant drugs such as the SSRIs (see *Chapter 4*). Because ketamine is a legal medicine in most countries (though 'illegal' for recreational use in most western ones) it was easy for doctors to obtain. In the US clinics sprang up in many cities, some being run by private psychiatrists and some even by anaesthesiologists. In the UK, Dr Rupert McShane in Oxford has run a ketamine clinic for several years and finds up to a third of his patients, all of whom have been resistant to prior treatments, respond to a course of four-to-eight IV ketamine injections over two-to-four weeks given by an anaesthetist. His model is that for some people ketamine can replace ECT. And because of this, and to save anaesthetists time (and hence costs), he conducts his ketamine clinic alongside his ECT treatments in the same clinical suite.

This rather medical approach of IV ketamine administration in a hospital setting under the care of an anaesthetist plus a psychiatrist is expensive and so other models of ketamine treatment have developed, especially in the US. Some psychiatrists now give the ketamine infusion by themselves in their out-patient clinics arguing that the doses used are sub-anaesthetic and so don't require an anaesthetist to be present. Others use an intra-muscular injection, something that even a psychiatrist can do unaided! Professor Paul Glue and his team in Dunedin, New Zealand have developed an oral tablet of ketamine which also seems to work and may soon be available.

Ketamine is the first pharmacologically novel anti-depressant in over 30 years. Its efficacy coupled with this pharmacological novelty has led to interest from the pharmaceutical industry which up till then had largely given up depression research. Several new derivatives of ketamine have been tested and one, S-ketamine, an isomer of ketamine, has been extensively studied by Janssen. To avoid the need for injections they developed intranasal technology allowing the medicine to be 'shot' into the nose from where it is quickly absorbed (a number of other medicine are given by this route so the technology was already there).

After a long, challenging, and expensive series of trials in which they tried to optimise the dose and duration of treatment they have now made it to market. Esketamine, as it is now called, is given intranasally twice a week for a month or more until the response is maximised then its dose frequency can be reduced.

In many ways, ketamine is an improvement on ECT, especially as there is no seizure so little impact on memory. But ketamine has two main drawbacks. The first is that it is a dissociative anaesthetic. Even when used at sub-anaesthetic doses it can produce a strong dissociative experience in some patients. These often include bizarre images, feelings of going mad, powerlessness and an inability to move, plus feelings of changed body shape and size distortion. These are a result of ketamine blocking the normal function of glutamate dependent pathways in the brain so distorting and disturbing brain function. I believe it is this disruption that allows the breakdown of depressive thinking and so enables recovery. But many patients find it unpleasant and attempts are now being made to find analogues of ketamine that lift mood without the dissociative anaesthetic effects. Whether they will work or not remains to be seen.

The second much larger problem with ketamine is that it is a drug that is abused by some people. Well before ketamine became considered as an antidepressant it was being used recreationally for its psychological effects. A popular use of ketamine was to help with the come down from an MDMA (ecstasy) or cocaine facilitated rave. Ketamine would be taken, often in a group once they returned home from a rave. In addition to its psychologically interesting effects ketamine also helps bring people down from the stimulants so they can sleep. The more people use ketamine recreationally the more likely they are to develop tolerance to these effects. This means they have to take larger and larger doses to get an effect. An initial 200mg dose might gradually need to be increased to a gram or more to get the same pleasurable experiences. Once tolerance has developed they will often discover they can't stop using because they get withdrawal reactions. They have become dependent or addicted to ketamine and now can't stop.

Once dependence kicks in users find they are taking huge doses of ketamine, on a daily basis, which leads to two big problems. The most dramatic and painful are the bladder spasms. These are widely known in the ketamine community as k-cramps and were once seen as a proof that the ketamine being used was potent and from a good source. They are cramps across the lower part of the abdomen that lead to a desire to pee, an experience anyone who has ever had cystitis will know only too well.

Initially these symptoms disappear after the ketamine has been cleared from the body, but as dosing spirals upwards they become more and more persistent and painful. Eventually the reason for them becomes apparent with blood in the urine. Ketamine has produced a form of chronic cystitis with severe bloody (haemorrhagic) inflammation of the bladder that slowly destroys it. The bladder shrinks and gets more damaged until eventually the person is in perpetual pain and leaking bloody urine. By then it's too late as the bladder can't ever recover even if they stop using ketamine. The only solution is removing it surgically. This gets rid of the pain but leaves the person with a catheter in the abdomen that drains urine from the kidneys into a bag. These catheters are hard to keep permanently clean, so on occasions bacteria creep in, leading to repeated kidney infections. The overall impact of these infections will be to shorten a person's life by ten-to-15 years.

The other less publicised but maybe more problematic impact of ketamine dependence and heavy use is that of brain damage. Professor Val Curran at University College London has shown that heavy users of ketamine develop a state of marked cognitive deterioration. It seems that the heavy use of this glutamate blocker leads to damage to the frontal parts of the brain—those involved in thinking, planning and decision-making. Dependent ketamine users are impaired in many of these tasks and often show a profile of cognitive impairment similar to that found in patients with schizophrenia. This is perhaps unsurprising since, for decades, animal researchers have used repeated doses of glutamate antagonists pharmacologically similar to ketamine in rodents to model cognitive deficits of schizophrenia.

At present we have no idea how to ameliorate these problems of cognition in people with ketamine addiction. Though I am hopeful that new treatments for schizophrenia, or even dementias, might also help them. In fact, because of the overlap in cognitive deficits seen in heavy ketamine users and people with schizophrenia I have suggested that these ketamine-damaged people might be a useful group in which to explore new treatments to enhance or repair cognitive function. This group has several advantages over people with schizophrenia. We know what has caused their problem, i.e. unlike people with schizophrenia they all have both the same and a guaranteed diagnosis. Also, they are free from medications that are used for people with schizophrenia such as antipsy-chotic drugs. These medicines can directly affect cognition themselves and may complicate the study of new drug treatments through interactions between the different sorts of drug treatments.

These challenges will limit the widespread use of ketamine. It's unlikely it will ever become as widely used as the SSRIs for depression. The risk of recreational misuse can be overcome by for example just giving it in doctors' surgeries or perhaps in high street pharmacies. Ketamine has already become something of a revolution in the treatment of depression because of its novel mechanism and fast action. The search is now on for other drugs that have the same rapid effects though ideally with longer durations of action. In *Chapter 13* we shall see how the psychedelic drug psilocybin may fit this bill.

CHAPTER 3

Revealing Anxiety Through Reframing Benzodiazepines

The rat twitched — but only ten seconds into the infusion. Had something gone wrong? Maybe just an outlier? I set the next one up, started the infusion and again this one also twitched early — about 12 seconds in. The same pattern was repeated with the next six rats — all twitched within 12 seconds of the infusion. But over the past year I had established in many experiments that normally rats didn't twitch for 25 or more seconds after the infusion started.

Even more perplexing was that we had predicted that the new 'natural' benzodiazepine drug we had treated each rat with would delay the time to twitch, just like synthetic anti-convulsant benzodiazepines such as diazepam. Something fundamentally strange was happening, this new 'natural' benzodiazepine was making rats more susceptible to seizures not less. My colleague Phil Cowen and my supervisor Richard Green were equally perplexed — had we done something wrong? How could a benzodiazepine not be anti-convulsant? Even more puzzlingly, how could it shorten the time to twitch, i.e. be pro-convulsant? It took us several years to unravel this mystery and, in the process, discover a whole new area of pharmacology and neuroscience, that had direct relevance to the question of why people are anxious or epileptic.

Our experiment was conducted in 1980 when benzodiazepines were at their peak of being prescribed. In the 1960s they had revolutionised many aspects of medicine. Their safety in overdose meant that they had replaced the much more toxic barbiturates (that had killed Marilyn Monroe amongst many others) as the sleeping pill of choice; no more deaths in the Valley of the Dolls! Benzodiazepines such as Valium (diazepam) and Librium (chlordiazepoxide) had become widely used as tranquillisers for daytime anxiety ('Mother's little helpers' in the words of the Rolling Stones). They had also had a major impact in neurology because of their profound anti-convulsant and anti-spasticity activity. For two decades they were the most prescribed medicines in the world, but how did they work?

One theory was that they mimicked or augmented a naturally occurring calming chemical that was made by our brain. A few years before I started my research, receptors for morphine had been found in the brain and soon after that the natural (endogenous) versions of morphine had also been discovered. These are small peptides called endorphins which we now know are released in the brain to help us cope with states of stress and pain. Opiate drugs like morphine and heroin bind to the same receptor as the endorphins to reduce pain, but also when taken by people not in pain can give pleasure (a high). The discovery of the endorphin system was one of the great advances in neuroscience, and it opened-up the possibility that all psychiatric and neurologic medicines might act on specific receptors in the brain.

Soon after, Claus Braestrup a PhD student in Denmark used radioactive-labelled diazepam to reveal that there were binding sites for this and the other clinically used benzodiazepines in the mammalian brain. It seemed our brains were designed to be receptive to benzodiazepines—but why? Did God have shares in the pharmaceutical giant Roche? The simplest explanation was that there were naturally occurring benzodiazepines (so called endozapines) in our brains. These would be to anxiety and epilepsy what the endorphins had been to pain and stress—the natural cures!

The hunt to find them was on and Braestrup decided to see if he could locate these endozapines in urine, because this was much easier to source than human brain material! He persuaded other members of his lab to collect their urine and from a total of 1,500 litres he began to extract organic molecules into the solvent ethyl acetate, then separated them into different portions using chromatography. He then tested these extracts against the binding of diazepam to its receptor; most had no impact but to his delight one did, and with even higher affinity than diazepam. He rapidly identified this as the b-carboline ethyl acetate (b-CCE for short) and published his findings in the leading journal *Nature*. The natural anxiolytic had been found—or had it?

We read this exciting new report and at the time were working with a chemist, Ian Martin, who was able to quickly synthesise b-CCE for us. We put it into the rats in an assay I had developed to explore the anti-convulsant effects of benzodiazepines. I infused a solution of a convulsant drug (bicuculline) until they had the start of a seizure—the first twitch. It had proved a reliable measure of the anti-convulsant effects of benzodiazepines and other anti-epilepsy drugs; these markedly prolonged the time to the first twitch. So we were ready to use it and explore the presumed anti-convulsant effects of the endozapine b-CCE, which we predicted would also delay the time to twitch.

But b-CCE wasn't anti-convulsant—unlike diazepam it didn't elevate the seizure threshold by delaying the time to the first twitch—it shortened it. In other words, it had an action exactly opposite to that of benzodiazepines. Once we had clearly established that b-CCE was pro-convulsant we began to wonder would it have opposite effects to the other actions of the benzodiazepines especially the anxiolytic ones?

To address this question I made contact with a team at the School of Pharmacy in London, Sandra File and Richard Lister, who were experts on anxiety in rodents. They were pleased to collaborate but only on the condition that I did the experiments with them when their labs were free. This meant on a Saturday morning. So I made several 5 am starts from Oxford, driving on thankfully empty roads, to Bloomsbury in London for a 6.30 am start of the rat testing. They explained that their anxiety testing was most reliable early in the morning and so we all had to work around this inconvenience. Still the experiments went smoothly, the control rats behaved as before, the benzodiazepines had their usual anxiolytic activity, so we had a reliable assay for b-CCE.

Their main model of benzodiazepine's anxiety-reducing (anxiolytic) effects in rats was the social anxiety test. Two stranger rats were put together in a cage and the amount of time they spent close together, sniffing and exploring each other, was recorded. Rats, like humans, are naturally shy of strangers and in this novel situation spent relatively little time in contact. After a benzodiazepine such as Librium (chlordiazepoxide) they were less anxious, so spent more time in contact, just like humans do when they are given an anxiolytic (especially alcohol!).

We wondered what would b-CCE do? Would it behave like a benzodiazepine or would it have the opposite effects as we had seen in the anti-convulsant testing? We found to all our surprise the opposite effects to the benzodiazepine. Whereas chlordiazepoxide increased social interactions, b-CCE reduced them. So, in two quite separate models of benzodiazepine function b-CCE had opposite effects. This was an unusual and unexpected set of data and when we presented it at UK pharmacological meetings it caused some perplexity in the pharmacology community. What did it tell us about how benzodiazepines worked? Why would the brain make b-CCE, a substance with effects opposite to synthetic drugs such as Valium? One idea was that b-CCE was a compound that woke us up in the morning and kept us alert during the day, and if present in excess might cause anxiety and seizures.

In conventional pharmacology a drug that activates a receptor (e.g. morphine) is called an agonist and a drug that blocks receptors is called an antagonist (e.g. naloxone). The degree to which either drug binds to the receptor is defined by its affinity. The higher affinity the more it binds — the more it sticks to the receptor. So could b-CCE be an antagonist to endozapines that was naturally helping to keep the brain calm and stop it having seizures? This seemed plausible as antagonists to known calming neurotransmitters particularly GABA and glycine did cause seizures. In fact I was using the GABA antagonist bicuculline to induce seizures that benzodiazepines would block to measure their activity.

The b-CCE as a benzodiazepine antagonist theory was short lived. The next year Roche published a paper on another benzodiazepine called flumazenil proving that this really was a benzodiazepine receptor antagonist. Flumazenil had been made in the 1950s along with a wide range of compounds with the benzodiazepine structure such as diazepam and chlordiazepoxide. However, it had no activity in the animal tests that at the time were the only means to determine the pharmacological effects of benzodiazepines. Flumazenil was then shelved until the receptor was identified when it was discovered to have even higher affinity for it than diazepam. By analogy with the opioid receptor the antagonist naloxone has no activity, but the agonist heroin does. The Roche team reasoned that flumazenil might be an antagonist — and they were right. Flumazenil proved extremely effective at reversing the effects of diazepam and other benzodiazepine agonists. It would instantly wake up rats and monkeys from diazepam-induced sleep, and it also reversed the anti-convulsant actions of benzodiazepines.

In fact flumazenil was so good a reversal agent that it was developed as a treatment in anaesthetic practice and is still widely used today. Many short surgical and investigative cases like endoscopies are conducted under the benzodiazepine midazolam given intravenously. Once the procedure is over the anaesthesia is reversed by an injection of flumazenil so the patient wakes up. This reversal effect is almost immediate and complete. I can testify to its efficacy because once I was unconscious under midazolam for an EEG experiment and was then reversed by flumazenil in time to give a lecture five minutes later!

The paradox with flumazenil is that by itself it had no obvious effects on the brain, which explains why it had been discarded as a possible therapeutic when first made. This absence of an effect of flumazenil meant that our idea that there was an endozapine that b-CCE blocked seemed unlikely, though it might still have been the case that, as with the endorphins, such a substance would only be made in times of severe stress, e.g. during a seizure.

An even more intriguing discovery we made was that flumazenil not only blocked the effects of diazepam but also the opposite effects of b-CCE. This finding proved a real challenge to explain and so we came up with a novel theory. We suggested that the benzodiazepine receptor was bi-directional in action. Benzodiazepine agonists like diazepam would turn it on, b-CCE would turn it off, and flumazenil would block the binding of both to the benzodiazepine receptor so being a neutral antagonist. When we presented this theory at the British Pharmacological Society meeting it caused a great stir. Senior members of the society were critical, phrases such as 'No way this could work,' 'Never been described before' were thrown at us in a quite hostile fashion. But soon we were proved right because the Roche group replicated our work and confirmed the bi-directionality of the benzodiazepine receptor. A new concept of pharmacology was born — the anti-agonist. We initially called b-CCE and related compounds *contragonists* because their effects were contrary to the actions of agonists. The Roche group invented the term *inverse agonist*. The influence and power of a huge pharmaceutical company such as Roche in a field which they had effectively invented, eventually prevailed over our small group and the term inverse agonist is now the accepted one.

From this episode in my research career I learnt an important lesson that has been replicated at other times, e.g. with the psychedelic research discussed in *Chapter 12*. If your experiment produces results that are *exactly opposite* to what you were predicting then they are almost certainly correct. There is no scope for subjective bias or manipulating the statistics to find a weak but significant result. In such cases rethink your theories because maybe you have discovered something much more exciting than you had previously conceived!

A most important accident in anxiety research

The concept of an inverse agonist has had huge influence in several areas of neuroscience. Although b-CCE turned out not to be an endozapine — it was probably created in the ethyl acetate extraction process and no endozapines have yet been found. But inverse agonism has been shown to explain many features of the effects of benzodiazepine and to contribute to disorders such as seizures, and in an accidental but remarkable experiment, produce severe anxiety.

The accidental anxiety experiment occurred whilst we were conducting our experiments that revealed b-CCE had opposite effects to diazepam i.e. was pro-convulsant and anxiogenic in rodents. However, before our findings were published Braestrup had linked up with the German pharmaceutical company Schering-Plough to develop b-CCE and related b-carbolines as treatments for anxiety. As inverse agonists or antagonists at the benzodiazepine receptor had never been postulated previously, let alone discovered, they assumed that any-thing that bound to the benzodiazepine receptor must be like diazepam — an agonist.

As a medicine, b-CCE was not a suitable candidate: it contains an ester group that would mean it would be rapidly broken down in the blood to inac-tive products. So the Schering-Plough chemists did what medicinal chemists often do to slow down the metabolism of a drug, they replaced the ester with a more stable amide group. The resulting compound was called FG7142 and was tested in the age-old procedure that pharmaceutical companies at that time (the early-1980s) used to estimate the effects of new drugs — it was taken by staff members in gradually increasing doses. The first few doses of FG7142 had no effect so the dose was increased until something happened which, when it did, it did so with a vengeance. Some time after taking the FG7142 the unsuspect-ing volunteer who was at the time in a committee meeting began to feel odd, surges of anxiety swept through his body and brain. He felt short of breath and started pacing around the room trying to calm himself down. He told his colleagues he was fearful, and they were surprised and somewhat disbeliev-ing — maybe he was being weedy, was it all psychosomatic?

Still, as planned, they took blood to measure the levels of FG7142 with enough spare to also allow them to measure stress hormones as well, which later turned out to be a wise move! They also filmed part of the anxiety episode.

After 40 minutes or so the anxiety subsided and the volunteer went back to work and a decision was made to repeat the same dose on another experienced volunteer the next day. The second volunteer was also a senior member of the drug development team who had years of prior experience of different sorts of experimental drugs. He was given the same dose of FG7142 as the previous one and before the hour was out he too had developed severe anxiety. He had to stop his meeting to pace about rubbing his chest and trying to breath more deliberately to control the fear that was building up inside him. But this didn't help and he became more and more terrified until at last he pleaded to be given an injection of a benzodiazepine to stop his feelings. This they did and soon after this intravenous injection the anxiety abated and he recovered his composure. A blood sample for plasma FG7142 concentrations and stress hormone levels was also taken.

When the blood tests were analysed it was found that these two volunteers had much higher plasma concentrations than any of those given lower doses of FG7142 — which explains why only they experienced the pharmacological effects of the drug. Also the stress hormone levels in these two were significantly elevated, again in contrast to the findings in the earlier volunteers. The conclusions were clear — FG7142 was an inverse agonist that when it reached a critical level in the blood would then occupy sufficient brain receptors to reveal its opposite actions to a benzodiazepine agonist. As an inverse agonist it would cause anxiety rather than reduce it. The increased blood levels of stress hormones supported the view that this effect was truly a biological one, not just a psychological response to a new drug.

These two volunteers were highly experienced drug researchers who had tested out many different kinds of drugs over the years, including several potential new treatments for brain disorders that their company had made. They were knowledgeable about drugs and confident in their own abilities to understand drug effects. Despite this high level of prior drug experience they both said they had never felt anything like the effects of FG7142 before. Despite knowing that their anxiety was 'just' due to a drug they were unable to control it using the usual cognitive approaches of self-reassurance, muscle relaxation and deep breathing. It seemed that the FG7142 had tapped into and activated a primitive anxiety circuit that could override any cognitive control. They had experienced pure terror from switching off, or turning down, the benzodiazepine receptor.

Neither of them ever forgot the experience and both refused to view the film record of their anxiety ever again. The memory of the terror they had experienced was so powerful they never wanted to re-live it. We would now say that they had developed PTSD from their exposure to FG7142. With hindsight they probably wish they had done some rodent anxiety experiments with FG7142 before giving it to themselves!

Although the effects of FG7142 were reported in just two people they were so profound and important that a report of them was published in the *Lancet*, the leading medical journal. This report is a landmark publication because it represents the first ever demonstration that anxiety could be mediated by a specific receptor in the brain. It also killed the idea that b-CCE and related b-carbolines were going to replace benzodiazepines in medicine! However FG7142 became a useful tool for basic research into inverse agonism because it could be used via the intraperitoneal rather than the IV route, and I took this up with enthusiasm.

And finally, it was definitive proof in humans of the concept of inverse agonism; our rodent work had proved predictive of the human situation. It was a pity that the Schering-Plough researchers hadn't conducted similar studies before testing in humans. But then again if they had they might never have gained ethical approval for giving FG7142 to humans. So, we might never have gained proof of inverse agonism in humans. The accidental exposure proved hugely important in terms of the pharmacology of the benzodiazepine receptor in humans.

But did it have any implications for anxiety disorders in humans? This question sat with me for a couple of years as I completed the research for my thesis and then I set out to test it when I went back into the clinic. In the meantime, I set out to work out just what our new concept of a bi-directional benzodiazepine receptor meant for pharmacology.

How inverse agonists revealed the complexities of benzodiazepine tolerance and withdrawal

Tolerance to benzodiazepines is well-known. When treating epilepsy patients with these drugs one often needs to increase the dose as seizures break thorough after a while. Even more apparent is withdrawal from benzodiazepines when they are stopped. Again, in patients with epilepsy this can take the form of a severe worsening of their seizures, and in the case of patients with anxiety a recurrence of their worries or panic attacks. Many people who use benzodiazepines for insomnia find that they have worse sleep when they stop, at least for a few days. This is called 'rebound insomnia.' These clinical phenomena are problematic and so during my research with the help of Hilary Little and my first PhD student, Stuart Taylor, I decided to study the nature of benzodiazepine tolerance and withdrawal in rats, using the new tools we had, b-CCE and flumazenil.

The first question we addressed was what happens when you give an inverse agonist repeatedly — do you get tolerance as with agonist benzodiazepines? The answer was no, just like with the immediate effects of inverse agonists, what you get is the opposite to agonists. In this case this was sensitisation to their effects. This means that a dose which at first has no obvious impact, over a week or so with daily administration eventually resulted in seizures. This phenomenon is called 'kindling' and had been seen previously with repeated electrical stimulation of some parts of the rodent brain. This was the first-time kindling had been shown for a specific receptor-acting drug. And we knew the inverse agonist kindling was mediated via the benzodiazepine receptor because we could block it with the antagonist flumazenil.

On the other hand, flumazenil given repeatedly had no effects at all, it was just as inert as when used for the first time. This proved that binding to the receptor was not sufficient to induce changes in its function, probably because there were no endozapines for the flumazenil to block. However, when diazepam or another benzodiazepine agonist was given for several weeks, then flumazenil did have noticeable effects — it would precipitate a withdrawal reaction with anxiety, shakiness and a lowered seizure threshold. This was the same set of symptoms that were seen with just stopping a repeated treatment with diazepam. But now it came on immediately the flumazenil was injected, not over several hours, a phenomenon known as precipitated withdrawal. Since then flumazenil precipitated withdrawal has been shown in humans who have been using benzodiazepines. It is similar in mechanism to the way in which naloxone will precipitate withdrawal from opiates by displacing an agonist from its receptor so revealing underlying changes in function.

The obvious question to me was, then, what happens if you treat rats repeatedly with a benzodiazepine agonist or with an inverse agonist? Does tolerance to an agonist also produce tolerance to an inverse agonist? It didn't take long to discover that the reality was different, again the opposite. When rats that had been exposed daily to a benzodiazepine for a week or more were given an inverse agonist (either b-CCE or FG7142) they had seizures, whereas before the diazepam treatment none had been seen. We concluded that the process by which benzodiazepine tolerance led to withdrawal reactions was somehow sensitising rats to the inverse agonists. We tried a number of different benzodiazepines and found the same results — the effects of FG7142 were enhanced. Normally this never produces seizures in naïve animals but in ones repeatedly exposed to benzodiazepines it could.

The simplest explanation was that the benzodiazepine receptor had somehow changed so that the effects of the agonists were attenuated (so producing tolerance) and the effects of the inverse agonist enhanced — maybe like the sensitisation we had seen with repeated administration of inverse agonists. We measured the number of the benzodiazepine receptors in the rat brains and found no difference in number so whatever was happening was at the level of receptor function rather than the number of available receptors.

Then it occurred to us that if the receptor function had changed for both agonists and inverse agonists than maybe the effects of an antagonist would also be altered. This meant giving flumazenil to animals that were benzodiazepine tolerant and seeing if it was still inactive. This was more complicated than at first sight because we had to ensure that we only gave the flumazenil after the diazepam had completely cleared from their brains, so the effects of the flumazenil were not confounded by possible precipitated withdrawal. This involved waiting for several days for the drug to clear. The wait was worth it for we found for the first time that flumazenil had activity. In these benzodiazepine-tolerant rodents, flumazenil actually reduced the seizure threshold — it was pro-convulsant (though it never provoked seizures).

Now how to make sense of all these findings? We developed a new theory of benzodiazepine receptor functionality by suggesting there was a spectrum of activity for drugs across the benzodiazepine receptor. On one side there were agonists like diazepam — in the middle antagonists like flumazenil — and at the other end inverse agonists like FG7142. Agonists were anxiolytic and anti-convulsant because they enhanced the effects of the brain's natural calming neurotransmitter GABA. Inverse agonists were anxiogenic and pro-convulsant because they decreased the activity of GABA. Flumazenil the antagonist had no effect either way except when the normal balance of receptor activity had somehow been changed.

Our theory predicted that the tolerance which developed after repeated administration of diazepam and other benzodiazepine agonists was due to the functionality of the spectrum moving in the inverse agonist direction. This means that the effects of the agonist were reduced (tolerance) those of the inverse agonist enhanced (sensitisation) and the previously neutral antagonist flumazenil became a little inverse. With this theory we now could explain why benzodiazepine tolerance led to anxiety and seizures in withdrawal—the receptor was less functioning.

Two new questions emerged—could we reverse these receptor changes and so prevent tolerance and withdrawal? And could anxiety and seizure disorders develop because of some abnormality of this receptor spectrum? We set out to answer the first in rodents and then, when I went back to the clinical arena, to answer the second question in patients.

How could we stop the spectrum shift that led to tolerance and withdrawal? One approach developed by Adam Doble at the French pharmaceutical company Rhône-Poulenc was to find benzodiazepine agonists with a different, non-benzodiazepine, chemical structure that did not sensitise rats to inverse agonists. He achieved this with the 'clone' series of compounds, one of which, zopiclone is now a widely used sleeping pill. This isn't totally free of tolerance and withdrawal but its active component (enantiomer) eszopiclone has been shown to be effective with little withdrawal even after a year of use. In anxiety disorders we showed that the 'clone' drug pagoclone had efficacy in stopping panic attacks but this and other analogues never really made it as alternative anxiolytics to the benzodiazepines.

This was more for commercial than pharmacological reasons; by the time they were being developed a hostile public swing against the benzodiazepines had started, with lawsuits against the pharmaceutical manufacturers, doctors and even the National Health Service (NHS). This was the biggest class-action lawsuit in world history that in the end came to nothing: a report by Lord Justice Kennedy found the enduring therapeutic benefits of the benzodiazepines clearly outweighed their transient drawbacks of withdrawal symptoms. However, it took over a decade for this situation to be resolved and this period of uncertainty meant that pharmaceutical companies and health authorities had little appetite for new benzodiazepine receptor-acting drugs for anxiety. Also, as we shall see in the next chapter, the SSRI anti-depressants were becoming established as anxiolytic treatments also and these had fewer unwanted effects and also treated any co-existing depression as well.

Still today the inverse agonist sensitising test is used by pharmaceutical companies working in the benzodiazepine receptor field to identify new receptor agonist drugs that have a low propensity to produce withdrawal and dependence such as partial agonists. These are drugs that have less activity at the receptor than the classic benzodiazepines such as diazepam so are predicted to have less problems of sedation, tolerance, and withdrawal. They certainly do have an improved tolerability profile in animal tests and several new selective partial agonists are under exploration for conditions such as anxiety and stuttering.

Anxiety in the clinic — Could the benzodiazepine receptor be to blame?

Having spent over three years of my research thesis investigating the role of the benzodiazepine receptor in anxiety and seizures it was natural that when I went back to my clinical training as a psychiatrist I would focus on patients with anxiety. There are plenty of these and my head of department Professor Michael Gelder was a world authority in this field. Along with Isaac Marks at the Institute of Psychiatry in London, a couple of decades before, he had pioneered the concept of exposure therapy as a treatment for phobias such as agoraphobia. This involved encouraging patients to experience their phobic situation — for example in the case of agoraphobia a supermarket — and remain there until their anxiety subsided, after which they were cured.

When Gelder returned to Oxford to set up the Department of Psychiatry he turned it into a world-leading centre for anxiety treatment research especially using the newly invented cognitive behavioural therapy (CBT) approach. This uses reasoning and cognitive control as well as exposure to help people overcome their anxieties. The psychologists David Sharp and Paul Salkovskis, who were then in the Oxford psychiatry department alongside me, were developing a theory on the cognitive causes of panic disorder. They suggested that people with panic attacks had a special cognitive problem—they were predisposed to having *catastrophic cognitions.* These are thoughts of serious medical outcomes that emerge as a result of some peripheral sensation. For example, a patient might feel a slight flutter of their heart and fear that they are having a heart attack. This is plausible for most healthcare professionals know it's common for panic predisposed individuals to call the emergency services or attend casualty departments for minor or non-existent medical problems.

Certainly, their theory accorded with some of my patients. I vividly recall one of my first patients with panic disorder. She was 21-years-old and very frightened of any changes in her heart rate which she interpreted as potentially the prelude to a heart attack, despite this being almost unheard of in someone her age without existing heart disease. Another young woman was terrified of getting short of breath because she thought this would lead to an asthma attack. To avoid getting breathless she began to reduce her exertions and of course this led to her becoming less and less fit, so whenever she did almost any activity she became short of breath. In the end, even vacuuming her house caused her to get breathless and then panic.

Each were ideal candidates for CBT but equally also they responded well to treatment with medicines. How could we reconcile these two seemingly quite different approaches to treatment? Did the medicines change their cognitions or did the CBT affect their brain in the same way a medicine did? Were there biological differences in the brains of people with panic disorder that made them predisposed to panic? Was there an area in their brain that was hyper-excitable and so produced a panic attack, in an analogous way to the situation in people with epilepsy where hyper-reactive regions produce seizures? And, if so, could changes in the benzodiazepine system be responsible?

The CBT psychological approach does not require or postulate a specific biochemical brain alteration predisposing to anxiety disorders, so my ideas were somewhat heretical. I was intrigued by the possibility that changes in the benzodiazepine receptors in the brain might underpin, indeed explain, why some people experience extreme anxiety disorders. This would explain why benzodiazepines work in them and also why people got more anxiety when they were stopped. The theory was quite simple and had empirical support from the accidental trial with FG7142, where switching down the benzodiazepine system caused profound anxiety. But how to test it? How could we measure benzodiazepine receptor function in the brains of people with an anxiety disorder and see if it was different from that of a normal non-anxious control group? But by then I had left Oxford to head up clinical research at the National Institute of Alcohol and Alcoholism at the NIH in the US, so testing my ideas had to wait till I returned to the UK to open my own research unit in Bristol University two years later in 1988.

From a clinical perspective altered benzodiazepine receptor sensitivity in anxiety patients was already known. Psychiatrists treating patients with severe anxiety such as panic disorder would often have to use high doses of benzodiazepines such as diazepam or alprazolam; doses that would put non-anxious people to sleep. It seemed that anxiety patients were pre-tolerant to the benzodiazepines, so maybe their receptor spectrum was already set in the inverse agonist direction? But could we perform a more scientific assessment?

Reflecting on our discovery that benzodiazepine tolerance was associated with flumazenil becoming somewhat inverse in activity I wondered what effect flumazenil would have in patients with anxiety disorders. If my theory was correct, and their spectrum was set in the inverse agonist direction then flumazenil would cause anxiety in them. Luckily by this time flumazenil had come into UK medicine as a reversal agent for sedative anaesthesia so we could easily obtain it from our pharmacy.

My clinical research team of Drs Paul Glue and Chris Lawford set out to recruit people with a panic disorder for testing. Of course, they had to be free of benzodiazepines for many weeks to avoid any risk of precipitating benzodiazepine withdrawal, as well as free from other drugs such as anti-depressants that might affect their brain responses. They also had to be prepared to have a needle put into a vein so we could infuse the flumazenil (which came as a solution). Often, anxiety patients are fearful of blood and needles, so this meant a few dropped out.

The experimental design was simple: in a randomised order blind to both the experimenter and patient, each patient was given an IV injection of either flumazenil or saline and their anxiety levels and physiological measures (heart rate and blood pressure) were measured for the next hour. In the end keeping them blind was difficult because so many of them panicked following one of the infusions. For once a prediction about the benzodiazepine receptor had turned out to be correct—flumazenil did cause over half of the panic disorder patients to panic just like our receptor spectrum shift theory predicted. None of the controls panicked. This was the first proof that an anxiety disorder was linked to a neurochemical change in the brain.

Why might panic disorder patients have abnormal benzodiazepine receptor functionality? We still don't know. It's possible that there are genetic factors at play. Panic is a moderately inherited disorder with identical twins showing over 50 per cent concordance for having the same problem. Also, patients' benzodiazepine receptor functions might be changed by them having been traumatised before they developed the disorder; this has been shown to occur in pre-clinical animal studies of stress. Or maybe the anxiety was an epiphenomenon, maybe panic patients would panic if they were given anything that altered their senses? Flumazenil wasn't totally inert in the normal controls for in a few people it produced a mild dizziness or light-headedness that lasted a few seconds. Could the panic disorder patients have just over-reacted to this and then developed a catastrophic cognition that then led to a panic attack like the CBT theorists predicted? Was there any way we could make a more direct investigation of the benzodiazepine receptor in the living brain of our patients?

In 1986 a conceptually remarkable paper was published showing a deficit of benzodiazepine receptors in the living brains of patients with focal epilepsy. This is a form of epilepsy that occurs as the result of brain damage—usually to the hippocampus. The Swedish investigators had used a brand new technique of positron emission tomography (PET) to measure the number of benzodiazepine receptors in different parts of the brain. The tracer they used was our old friend flumazenil but now labelled with a carbon 11 atom (most carbon is carbon 12). This enters the brain quickly and then sticks to the receptors for up to an hour. During this time most of the carbon 11 atoms disintegrate through radioactive decay. When they decay they release a positron, a positively charged electron. These don't travel a long way from their parent atom before they meet one of the trillions of electrons in the brain and fuse with it (opposite charges attract!). This fusion of positively and negatively charged electrons destroys both, but from this auto-destruction come two gamma rays that shoot off in opposite directions. These are powerful rays that leave the brain, pass through the skull and would disappear into space unless stopped. A PET scanner has a series of cells arranged in a ring around the head to collect and measure these gamma rays. Then with sophisticated mathematical reconstruction the origins of the rays can be pinpointed to the brain region they came from. More rays from a given region means more flumazenil binding to its receptors, i.e. more receptors.

Once a research tool, now in the top epilepsy centres, flumazenil PET is a standard clinical tool to help surgeons identify the site of seizure activity (the epileptic focus) in the brain before removing that part. It is also used to prove that drugs binding to the benzodiazepine receptor get into the brain and to identify the relationship between dose/plasma concentration and brain occupation so that optimal dosing of new benzodiazepines can be determined before expensive clinical trials are started.

The resolution of PET is impressive — down to just a few millimetres — so we can easily locate most brain regions thought to be involved in anxiety such as the hippocampus, amygdala, and sub-fields of the frontal cortex. It was thus ideal to measure these receptors in the brains of people with panic disorder. The good news was that there was a research unit in the UK that was making the tracer — the MRC Cyclotron Unit at the Hammersmith Hospital. The bad news was that we were in Bristol 120 miles away. But needs must and mostly through the efforts of an energetic and driven clinical research fellow — Andrea Malizia — and the help of Peter Liddle, an old colleague from Oxford, who was now at the Cyclotron Unit we were able to get the study done.

It wasn't easy. You can imagine the challenges we had to face. First, we had to find panic disorder patients who were free from benzodiazepines for months. In practice this turned out to be less problematic than we had expected because the BBC a few years earlier had created such a scare about benzodiazepine dependence that many of our patients were so frightened of them they never took any! We then had to ask our patients if they were interested in taking part in a research project. Most would say a cautious yes so then we had to explain the procedures. They would have to go to London for a scan (we would pay all costs), they would have to lie still with their head in a tub like large washing machine (the scanner) for 90 mins. We would stick a needle in a vein in one arm which they usually would accept. But then they would have a needle in an artery in the other wrist which they found more disturbing, but having been a subject for many PET scans by then I could show them my own multiple wrist scars to reassure them that it was safe (they are still there to this day).

The most challenging fact we kept until last — they would be given radioactivity. The word 'radioactivity' tends to worry many people more than it should. In reality a PET scan gives about as much radioactivity as one would get from living in Cornwall for about half a year (where radioactivity comes from the ground in the form of the gas radon).

Despite these challenges we achieved our target numbers by busing, driving and transporting people by rail from all over the UK. In the end, 13-and-a-half scans were conducted (the half scan was one woman who was so anxious she would only put her head halfway into the scanner! Still we could measure the receptors in the part that was inside and so use her data). Of course, we had to conduct scans in a similar number of age matched controls who were free of any anxiety or other psychiatric disorder.

After the last scan was conducted it took quite a few weeks of data analysis and number crunching to get the results and they were spectacular. Across most of the brain the panic patients showed significantly lower levels of flumazenil binding than the control group. This difference was most pronounced in the frontal anxiety circuit and, in one of these areas, there was a total separation of binding between patients and controls. The highest binding in any patient was lower than the lowest in the controls. This means that the amount of benzodiazepine binding in this brain region could be used to make the diagnosis of panic disorder. The only problem with this approach was the cost — about £10,000 for each scan makes it beyond the reach of most people and health insurers! I did have one patient who offered to pay personally for a scan but since I couldn't say that this would realistically alter my treatment plan I felt that to encourage him in this would be unethical.

Since our study, two other research groups, in the US, have repeated this approach and found essentially the same outcome — significant reductions in benzodiazepine receptor binding in anxiety-related brain regions in people with panic disorder. Such replications are an essential part of scientific research, for they give us much more confidence that an original finding was real. Two replications without any non-replications makes it almost certain that this is a general feature of people with panic disorder. So it seems clear that panic attacks come because the brains of people so-predisposed have a relative deficiency of the benzodiazepine receptor. As this is the main inhibitory system in the brain their brains are more excitable. People who experience panics differ from those with epilepsy in the location of this inhibitory deficit. In epilepsy the loss of benzodiazepine receptors is found in regions relating to seizure production such as the hippocampus and parts of the frontal cortex. In panic the deficits are in the anxiety circuit.

Both disorders share the common feature of being responsive to treatment with benzodiazepines such as diazepam (Valium). This to some extent rectifies the deficit of natural benzodiazepine receptor activity so stops seizures and panic attacks in a manner analogous to insulin treating diabetes by replacing what's missing. Unfortunately, these beneficial effects come at a price, one drawback is other effects of benzodiazepines such as sedation which can impair a patient's ability to think quickly and clearly. The other drawback is the phenomenon we saw earlier where repeated administration of a benzodiazepine agonist produces a shift in receptor function in the inverse agonist direction. This means that the effects of the benzodiazepine treatment tend to wear off over weeks or months. But worse is the problem that the change in receptor function can in some people when they stop the medicine lead to their disorder being worse than before during the withdrawal period. It seems that the benzodiazepines have in themselves an inevitable tendency to undermine their own actions by altering their own receptor function in the same direction as the disorder.

The analogy I like to use to explain the problems with benzodiazepines is that of a crack in a wall in your house. It may look unsightly and so you can chose to hide it from view using wallpaper, i.e. 'paper over the cracks.' This serves the short-term purpose of making the room look nicer and you may even forget you had a crack at all. But the wallpaper isn't fixing the crack and indeed the crack may be getting bigger beneath it! So, when the wall paper is removed the crack is as bad or maybe even worse than before. In some people benzodiazepines seem to sow the seeds of their own destruction, the receptor changes they produce undermine their therapeutic ability.

This worsening phenomenon on withdrawal from repeated benzodiazepine agonist doses doesn't seem to occur in all patients. For example, people given benzodiazepines for spasticity or muscle spasm or headaches don't seem to get a worsening when they stop. This I believe is because their original illness is not caused by alterations in the benzodiazepine receptor system. But other anxiety disorders and insomnia behave like panic and epilepsy with worsening in withdrawal, and so they may also be due to alterations in brain benzodiazepine receptor number also, though PET scanning studies have not been conducted to test this theory directly.

Is there anything we can do about this? Several experimental trials have been made to reverse or re-set the receptor changes though none have reached the stage of acceptable efficacy for clinical use. For instance, we tried using low doses of the benzodiazepine antagonist flumazenil to correct the receptor shift but ran into the problem of precipitated withdrawal being too distressing. Another approach is to use a less potent (partial agonist) version of benzodiazepines. These cause less receptor changes and so less withdrawal in animal studies. Pagoclone was one of these, and as we learned above one that had the added value of having a different chemistry that induced less tolerance. In a small proof-of-concept study we showed it could be effective in panic disorder but no big pharmaceutical company was prepared to invest the hundreds of millions of pounds needed to get through the regulatory hurdles, so it has never become a medicine.

After over a decade of trying to make sense of the benzodiazepine system and its role in brain disorders, I had made some considerable progress. We now knew how the benzodiazepine receptor worked, that there were drugs with opposite actions (the inverse agonists) and an antagonist with clinical utility (flumazenil) had been discovered. But benzodiazepines themselves, though useful treatments, left a lot to be desired because of their tendency to undermine their own actions and leave patients in a worse state when they were stopped. If we couldn't overcome this problem by novel benzodiazepine pharmaceutical approaches were there other neurotransmitters we could target to get better results? Perhaps the serotonin system was a better target than the benzodiazepine receptor? The answer to this is in the next chapter.

CHAPTER 4

Struggles with Serotonin

'Is it safe?' Professor Gelder asked.

'I think so,' Dr Cowen replied.
'Are you sure it's going to work?' the Prof responded.
From inside the research cubicle came a loud retort:
'If we knew it was going to work it wouldn't be research!'

This last remark was from me and I was about to have my serotonin system tested in a powerful way by my colleague and research partner Phil Cowen. The good news is I lived to tell the tale, but it was a rocky and revealing ride.

Serotonin is now a well-known neurotransmitter—in the same league of popular knowledge as are noradrenaline, dopamine and endorphins. It has become synonymous with depression and I have had patients tell me that they think they are serotonin deficient and would like it boosted by a selective serotonin re-uptake inhibitor (SSRI) drug such as Prozac or Seroxat. These medicines enhance the available amount of functional serotonin in the brain by preventing it being taken back up into the nerves from which it came. There is therefore more serotonin to act on the multitude of different serotonin receptors in the brain, which currently stand at 15, so more than for any other neurotransmitter. The plethora of different receptors means that serotonin can do many different things in the brain. In reality, serotonin is involved in almost all brain functions—from perception and cognition through to mood, sex and sleep. The only major brain functions that serotonin doesn't play much of a role in are movements and touch/balance.

So, what aspects of serotonin were we trying to study? In those days—the early 1980s—the drugs we used to treat depression were from the 1950s, either the tricyclics or the monoamine oxidase inhibitors (MAOIs). Both these classes of anti-depressant were discovered by serendipity. Each was being tested for another indication and observant clinicians noted that they had effects on mood. The first MAOI was isoniazid that was being developed as a treatment for tuberculosis. It had little effect on the lesions in the lungs but despite that did improve the patient's mood. Subsequently this and related compounds, e.g. phenelzine were tested and found effective in depressed people.

How anti-depressants revolutionised brain science

The first tricyclic anti-depressant was imipramine. This was derived from the sedative antihistamine and anti-psychotic drugs such as promazine and chlorpromazine and was being tested as a possible successor to chlorpromazine in schizophrenia. As with the MAOIs it didn't work in the primary indication but did improve the mood in these patients. Imipramine was rapidly taken in clinical psychiatric practice and soon after a whole series of related compounds such as amitriptyline, dothiepin, nortriptyline and protriptyline were made available. These new drugs were the first treatments specifically for depression, which till that point had been hard to treat except with electro convulsive therapy (ECT), so they revolutionised the treatment of this disorder. They also were found to have profound benefits in some forms of anxiety, especially in those with sudden fearful episodes such as panic attacks. But how did they work?

The 1950s was the dawn of the science of neurochemistry. It was becoming clearer that the brain was a machine made up of billions of nerves cells that used chemicals called neurotransmitters to communicate between each other (which in the brain we call neurons). Different chemicals were being discovered and one of the first was serotonin, or if one uses its chemical name 5-HT (5-hydroxytryptamine). The name serotonin indicates its first source—blood serum. It had been known for millennia that blood clots, if left to themselves, and blood vessels seal themselves when cut. In the search to determine what in the blood produced these effects a chemical was found in the blood serum that tightened blood vessels—hence the name sero-tonin. This was soon identified as the chemical 5-HT and soon after 5-HT was found in the brain and other organs, especially the gut.

The fact that the blood, and the gut, have lots of serotonin (both have much more than the brain) has always been a source of fascination for those with a psychosomatic bent. It's less surprising than at first sight since the gut and brain are from the same embryological tissues and, in both, serotonin is found as a neurotransmitter in nerves. But, in the gut, serotonin is also found in some immune cells (mast cells) and in blood platelets. Platelets are little packets of serotonin that float around in the blood until a blood vessel is damaged when they burst and release serotonin that then helps the clot form, and also constricts the damaged vessels to reduce bleeding.

Platelets have a remarkable ability to concentrate serotonin because they have special uptake sites for serotonin, the same sites as serotonin neurons have to collect the serotonin that they release and then repackage for future use. These sites allow platelets to scavenge serotonin from the blood and store it for when required. Almost all of the serotonin in the blood is in the platelet and anti-depressant medicines that work to block serotonin re-uptake in the brain also block it in the platelet. This reduces the total amount in the blood and is why use of drugs such as the SSRIs is associated with a slightly greater risk of bleeding problems.

For many decades the platelet was the easiest way to explore changes in serotonin function in the body. Taking blood was easy but taking brain samples was almost impossible for practical and ethical reasons. Also, when it became clear that the re-uptake processes in platelets and neurons were the same there was the hope that serotonin in the platelet might be a proxy for brain serotonin function. Maybe low levels of serotonin in the blood would predict low levels in the brain? For a while the idea that depressed people had a reduced number of re-uptake sites in their platelets was touted as a possible test (biomarker) for depression vulnerability but with more detailed analysis this turned out not to be the case. Still the platelet re-uptake site was easy to study and so a good assay for exploring the potency of different re-uptake blocking anti-depressants.

It was the discovery of tricyclic anti-depressants that led to the discovery of re-uptake sites. These drugs became widely used from the late-1950s to treat depression. They rapidly superseded the amphetamines for reasons of improved efficacy and safety, but we didn't know how they worked. The big breakthrough came with the discovery of the re-uptake sites by Les Iversen in the 1960s. By then it had become clear that the tricyclics somehow enhanced the effects of noradrenaline and Les, who was an inspiration to me when I was taught by him at Cambridge, did a simple experiment. He treated rats with imipramine then injected them with radioactive noradrenaline and measured how much radioactivity got into their brains. Surprisingly, the imipramine treated group had much lower amounts than the control group. But why? Les reasoned that imipramine was blocking the uptake of noradrenaline into brain tissue, and so inferred there must be an uptake process for this neurotransmitter, and then went on to prove this. Now we know there are many different re-uptake sites, each selective for a specific neurotransmitter, and so his discovery was one of the great conceptually transforming discoveries in neuroscience.

Soon other researchers were on his heels exploring if anti-depressants had an impact on the re-uptake of other neurotransmitters, and two Swedish groups, one including the eventual Nobel Laureate, Arvid Carlsson, discovered that imipramine not only blocked noradrenaline re-uptake but also that of serotonin. This finding raised an interesting question — was it enhancing noradrenaline or serotonin that led to the anti-depressant effect? It also posed the bigger question — was there a deficiency of one or other of these neurotransmitters in the brains of people with depression?

The first question was the easiest to solve because it proved relatively straightforward to make new chemicals that bound to and blocked these re-uptake sites. Some (e.g. desipramine) turned out to be much more active on the noradrenaline site, whereas others (e.g. clomipramine) preferred the serotonin one. In the clinic both turned out to be effective anti-depressants though with rather different side effect profiles. The noradrenaline acting anti-depressants tended to be more activating and the serotonin ones more calming. This early clinical insight had major implications for the later treatment of anxiety disorders for which serotonin re-uptake-blocking anti-depressants have now superseded the benzodiazepines as the medicines of choice.

However even the most serotoninergic of the tricyclic anti-depressants still had significant activity at the noradrenaline re-uptake site, so it wasn't proven that enhancing serotonin alone would be sufficient to lift mood. Someone had to take the plunge and make a purely serotonin-acting anti-depressant and the company that did this first was the Swedish one Astra (now part of Astra-Zeneca). They developed zimelidine, which turned out to be the first of the selective serotonin re-uptake inhibitors (or SSRIs). These medicines were to revolutionise the pharmacological treatment of both depression and anxiety disorders.

I vividly remember zimelidine becoming available for prescription. I was in my first year of psychiatry training and up to that point had gained a lot of experience with the tricyclics. These were effective treatments but had some significant adverse effects especially a dry mouth, blurred vision, constipation, weight gain and sedation. All of these were due to the fact that these drugs were all derivatives of older sedative antihistamines. Zimelidine being of a completely new, non-tricyclic, chemical structure was free from all of these. Patients who had struggled with the adverse effects of the tricyclics loved it when they were switched to zimelidine. They could think clearly, lost the weight they had gained previously and were able to speak crisply because their dry mouth disappeared.

Even more pleasing was the discovery that zimelidine was much, much safer in overdose. Depression is strongly associated with suicidal thoughts and up to 15 per cent of people with this mental disorder eventually kill themselves. At that time, it was common for depressed patients to overdose on their tricyclic anti-depressants and these were quite toxic, being responsible for many hundreds of overdose deaths per year. This overdose toxicity of the tricyclics was largely due to the same pharmacological actions that led to their side effects. Zimelidine was free of these unwanted actions and so was far less dangerous in overdose. This meant we could treat patients quite differently. Previously when we had fears over our patient's suicide risk we might only prescribe a few days tricyclics at a time, so they couldn't impulsively overdose. Now we could give a month's supply safe in the knowledge that even if a patient took the whole bottle little harm would come. Not only did this liberate us doctors from the fear of aiding our patients to kill themselves but also it helped reduce the stigma on our patients — having to go to the pharmacy every couple of days to protect you from yourself wasn't good for our patients' sense of self-worth.

A good example of this fundamental advance in the safety of anti-depressants came from an accusation from the mother of a patient of mine. She called me in my clinic where I had seen her and her daughter the week before and accused me 'of doing an experiment on her daughter.' Puzzled I asked why she thought this, and she explained that I had given her daughter a placebo! It turned out that the daughter had taken a whole month's supply of the SSRI paroxetine I had prescribed at the last visit and wasn't made ill by this overdose — hence the mother assumed it had been a placebo. The patient, her daughter was a woman in her late-20s who had before this taken many overdoses of tricyclics and each one had made her so ill that she required hospital admission, and was several times close to death. The mother presumed that all anti-depressants would be similarly toxic in overdose, but the SSRIs were very much safer.

This improvement in safety was the main benefit of the SSRIs—not only did it protect patients but also doctors. No longer did worrying about our patients' overdoses harming them dominate our interactions with them. We could now focus more on the issues driving or resulting from their depression, rather than simply keeping them alive. Since their introduction the SSRIs have saved millions of people from dying due to impulsive overdoses, and in countries like Scandinavia that rapidly switched all patients to them, the national suicide rates have fallen.

Sadly, the UK was slow to take up these new medicines, because they were more expensive than the older tricyclics, a pound a day rather than ten pence, and so we were one of the slowest of the western countries to switch to the SSRIs. During this transition period, which ran over several decades from the late-1980s, each year in the UK many hundreds of patients died needlessly from a tricyclic overdose. This was a health scandal of epic proportions that has largely been suppressed by the medical and other media.

Once zimelidine had established the principle that depression could be lifted by a drug acting specifically to elevate serotonin then several other companies began to develop similar medicines. These became some of the best-known medicines in history—drugs such as Prozac (fluoxetine), Seroxat (paroxetine) Lustral (sertraline) and Cipralex (citalopram) not just took over the treatment of depression but entered the public lexicon. Prozac even made the cover of *Time* magazine.

The reason for the popularity of the SSRIs was that they had many other advantages over the tricyclics in addition to their safety in overdose. Their side effect profile was so benign that for other people it was not obvious that the treated person was actually on a medicine. No longer was there the giveaway symptom of an always dry mouth with forgetfulness and sedation. Depressed people looked and sounded just like the rest of us.

Of course, the SSRIs weren't free of adverse effects in everyone, but these were generally hidden from public view. In some people they had an impact on sexual function by delaying orgasm, which was a concern for some people but for young men with premature ejaculation could be a benefit (and now SSRIs are sometimes prescribed for this purpose). Some people had vivid dreams or even insomnia. Others experienced some nausea and appetite suppression which could lead to slight weight loss. This was something that most patients found desirable and was in marked contrast to the tricyclics which often resulted in a lot of weight gain. Because of these effects on appetite and weight control Prozac was subsequently licensed for the treatment of the binge eating disorder bulimia nervosa.

It was this wide safety margin and enhanced tolerability of the SSRIs that made them the standard first-line treatment for depression, but it had other ramifications especially in the field of anxiety disorders. Shortly after the discovery of the MAOIs and tricyclics psychiatrists had begun to explore their utility in other disorders and several groups found that they could help patients with severe anxiety such as panic attacks and phobias. But this use was not developed for two reasons. First the benzodiazepines came along and reduced anxiety immediately whereas the anti-depressants took weeks to work. The other reason was that the side effects of the tricyclics were poorly tolerated by anxious people, and since the benzodiazepines didn't really have any immediate adverse effects these became the go to medicine for anxiety.

But over time, by the 1990s, it became clear that the benzodiazepines weren't as free of unwanted effects as had been assumed. Some people had problems with withdrawal when they tried to stop them and others found them too sedating, so a search began for a medicine to replace them. The SSRIs fitted the bill, if introduced gradually they were well-tolerated and over weeks and months patients found their anxiety symptoms slowly disappeared. Even better the SSRIs also lifted depression as well, which was a major benefit as depression is quite commonly associated with anxiety disorders. Now the SSRIs are the medicinal treatment of choice for all anxiety disorders from panic, social anxiety and OCD through to generalised anxiety disorder and PTSD.

My group was one of the pioneers of the use of SSRIs for anxiety disorders and the impact of these on our patients was often profound. People who had been housebound for years because of their fear of panics could start shopping again. Others disabled by worry could begin to enjoy a carefree life and those constrained by obsessional checking were liberated to do other more useful things. Most remarkable was their impact on marriage. We had a number of young male patients who developed severe anxiety once they had become engaged to be married. Their particular fear was the speech that they would have to make on their wedding day. They were terrified of making a fool of themselves in front of their friends and family. This experience is a common one in people with social anxiety disorder who often say that giving a talk is the worse thing they could ever do, even worse than dying.

Engagement anxiety has been recognised for several centuries, the Germans even have a term for it, *engagement psychose*. Often the anxiety is so overwhelming the man calls off the wedding. Before coming across cases of this in my anxiety disorders clinic I had seen an example at a family wedding when the groom received a round of applause as he got up to speak and then experienced what many patients with speaking anxiety fear — complete speech block. He opened his mouth but no words came out. A horribly embarrassing experience for him and for the rest of us who suffered for and with him but could do nothing to help.

Faced with the first case I had ever come across in my clinic I wondered if we could treat this problem as a form of social anxiety disorder, which we had begun to find the SSRIs were very effective in treating. So I explained to the worried groom-to-be my strategy. We would start him on a low sub-therapeutic dose of an SSRI for a couple of weeks to ensure he would tolerate them. If he did then we would increase the dose into the therapeutic range and hold it there up to the time of the wedding. It worked brilliantly, his anxiety subsided over the coming weeks and the wedding day speech was a great success. Subsequently I treated three more young men effectively with these medicines and each managed to achieve their wedding day goal.

The ability of the SSRI medicines to fundamentally change some peoples' ability to cope with the world was obvious to those prescribing the medicines. Over weeks or months patients who had been anxious and stressed about many aspects of their lives began to become more relaxed and outgoing. Some were able to return to work and perform better than before. Many teachers found that they were able to stave off premature retirement on the grounds of ill-health by gaining control of their moods and anxiety, to the benefit of many thousands of school students.

Similarly, I treated many GPs and other doctors with these medicines. For all my professional life UK medicine has been going through a series of organizational and procedural revolutions that challenge and often undermine their ability to perform their work to their satisfaction. Many would stay awake at night going over the patients they had seen in the day wondering if they made the right diagnosis and treatment decisions. Over time this anxiety would evolve into depression, their enjoyment of their work would dissipate, and they would begin to consider retiring on the grounds of ill-health. This is the worst possible outcome for the NHS as losing talented and experienced doctors is costly and wasteful. Some would turn to benzodiazepines to help reduce their anxiety and insomnia but often they would be concerned that the sedation and amnesia that these produced would make them more likely to make mistakes. The SSRIs helped them to get their anxiety and depression under control without impairing their cognitive abilities.

One other aspect of anti-depressant efficacy needs to be made clear. They are quite effective medicines for lifting depressed mood, with more than half of depressed patients responding moderately or very well, a similar proportion to responder rates in other medical disorders. But where anti-depressants show especial efficacy is in preventing recurrence of depression. When their use is maintained for months, or even years, in people who have recovered from depression they have a powerful effect to protect against further episodes. Anti-depressants including the SSRIs provide powerful protection against the underlying biochemical changes and the external life stresses that often lead to depression. This protective effect is one of the most powerful prophylactic actions known to medicine. We now know that the power of anti-depressants to prevent future episodes of depression is many times greater than that of statins to prevent future heart attacks. The power of a treatment is given by the 'number needed to treat statistic.' To prevent one new episode of depression we need to treat less than three patients with anti-depressants for several years whereas with statins the number needed to treat is over 20.

In recent years there has been a complete conceptual shift in our understanding of depression. We now know that for almost everyone depression is a recurrent condition. If they live long enough, over 95 per cent of people who have a first depressive episode will have another within 25 years. Many people have episodes each year or even more frequently. A patient of mine lost his job as a teacher when only 27-years-old because he'd had eight episodes of depression in the past five years and so had lost a lot of work time. Each episode responded well to an anti-depressant but, once he had recovered, his GP then assumed he was well and so stopped the medicine. Within a few weeks or months later his depression recurred. At that time, in the early-1990s, the concept of depression as a recurrent illness similar to diabetes or hypertension was only just beginning to be appreciated. Previously the medical profession had viewed depression like pneumonia or a broken leg as a one off illness. Now we know that we need to treat depression over the long-term to maximise recovery and prevent further episodes.

This gets us back to the second question — how does enhancing serotonin do this, and is there a defect in brain serotonin that underpins, or at least facilitates, the development of anxiety and depression? This was the reason I was being tested by Phil Cowen as described at the start of this chapter. We were trying to develop methods to examine the functioning of serotonin in the brain to address the key questions, is there a deficiency in people with depression and anxiety, and do the SSRIs and other anti-depressants rectify this?

Testing serotonin in the brain

The experiment I was the test-bed for was to see what happened if we enhanced serotonin in the brain, could we then get measures of serotonin receptor function that might differ in patients? I had been pre-treated the night before with the serotonin re-uptake blocker clomipramine and was about to get an infusion of l-tryptophan. This is an amino acid that is the precursor of serotonin in the brain. The only source of l-tryptophan in the brain is from the diet. It is found only in the proteins we eat and extracted from them by their breaking down in the liver. The l-tryptophan then passes into the blood and then the brain. But this passage is an active process, for just as there is a pump that sucks serotonin into neurons, there is a pump that sucks l-tryptophan, and other amino acids into the brain. Despite this active uptake the brain is relatively deficient in l-tryptophan. This the least prevalent of the vital amino acids, and some have argued that the human brain is always on the verge of l-tryptophan, and hence serotonin, deficiency. This is especially an issue in women as they have a more rapid breakdown of serotonin than men which may explain why they are more prone to depression.

Once the l-tryptophan gets into the brain it is rapidly converted to serotonin via the intermediary 5-HTP. This means that any limitation of l-tryptophan availability in diet will lead to the brain levels of l-tryptophan falling and so serotonin concentrations declining. Any reduction in protein in diet will therefore lead to a reduction in l-tryptophan in the brain and so in the production of serotonin. If this reduction is persistent as in starvation or even just with a low protein diet then serotonin function in the brain is reduced. Phil Cowen and Chris Fairburn in Oxford showed that just a few weeks of a 1,000 calorie per day diet reduced serotonin function in women's brains.

The vulnerability of brain serotonin to changes in l-tryptophan in the diet also helps explain why depression is more common in people with malnutrition and also in vegans, because of the low level of l-tryptophan in their diets. A common symptom of depression is a loss of appetite and this might then produce a vicious circle whereby low food intake leads to lower l-tryptophan in the blood and so to less serotonin in the brain, a situation that then exacerbates their depression or at least delays their recovery. I always encourage my patients to eat a balanced diet with plenty of protein to avoid any risk of them being serotonin deficient from low l-tryptophan.

We now know from our own and others' work, that in order for patients to stay well it is necessary to keep brain serotonin functioning elevated. Because the brain is always on the verge of serotonin deficiency any interruption in the supply of l-tryptophan will, within hours, lead to serotonin levels falling. There is a proven way of doing this called the tryptophan depletion approach. Phil Cowen and Katy Smith in Oxford showed that if serotonin is depleted by this approach then recovered depressed patients who were free of medicines or had even recovered just with CBT, will within five hours relapse. The group of Pedro Delgado and Dennis Charney in Yale showed the same impact of tryptophan depletion to provoke relapse in patients who had recovered on SSRIs. In all these experiments the mood can be rapidly restored by giving a high tryptophan meal, so there are no long-term effects of this transient interruption of serotonin production.

My own research into the brain mechanisms of anxiety found similar effects. Caroline Bell and Sean Hood in my group showed that when people have recovered from their panic or social anxiety disorder on an SSRI, this recovery can be temporarily interrupted by tryptophan depletion. For a few hours after l-tryptophan is depleted they become anxious again and are more likely to panic or become fearful when stressed. This is an important message — serotonin is necessary, even in some people vital, to keep depression and anxiety disorders at bay. This explains why people often relapse if they stop taking their anti-depressants; the underlying deficit in serotonin function has not fully recovered so without the SSRIs on board to promote serotonin levels they relapse.

The obvious question that derives from these observations, is would increasing l-tryptophan in one's diet help to improve mood or even treat depression or anxiety? Sadly, it's not that simple. Trials of l-tryptophan supplementation have not shown efficacy in depression possibly because relatively little actually gets into the brain (most is turned into protein or kynurenine by the liver). A more potent source is 5-HTP (5-hydroxytryptophan) which is the intermediate between l-tryptophan and serotonin. This is commonly sold in health food stores as a natural sleep promoting agent. It has been shown to help hold depression at bay but alone isn't strong enough to pull someone out of a depressive episode. However, both l-tryptophan and 5-HTP are able to boost the effects of anti-depressants such as the SSRIs and so are often given with them to augment their efficacy.

At the time of our research, which pre-dated the SSRIs, we knew that many anti-depressants would block serotonin re-uptake and clomipramine was the most potent of them, which is why we used it. So we reasoned that if we gave l-tryptophan on top of clomipramine we would get a significant serotonin boost in the brain, which we could then measure by looking at psychological and mood changes and also the release of hormones such as prolactin.

So Phil Cowen, reassured by my desire to get on with the research, opened-up the tap on the infusion set and began to infuse me with a litre of saline solution containing three gram of l-tryptophan. The serotonin boost wasn't long in coming. Within minutes the first wave of nausea swept over my throat. I wanted to vomit but couldn't. At ten minutes the first of the score sheets were read out to me:

'On a 0–100 scale how anxious do you feel?'
'Twenty,' I replied.

'And how sleepy?'

'Zero' I responded.

'And how nauseous?'

'Ninety-nine I replied'

'Are you sure?' came the question.

'Yes, I am and please bring me a vomit bowl asap!'

I remained at a score of 99 for nausea for many hours, sometimes retching but never able to get the relief I hoped would come if I had been able to vomit. The effects of the l-tryptophan plus clomipramine lasted all day and all night. I somehow managed to get home (did Phil drive me?). I slept hardly at all, tossing and turning through a series of vivid weird and colourful dreams and nightmares with lots of simple visual hallucinations of lights and colours in-between. By the next day most of the symptoms had subsided and I was able to get back to work and share these experiences with our research team. We all agreed that the l-tryptophan-clomipramine combination looked like a good way to enhance serotonin in the brain, but decided to use lower doses of each in future subjects to minimise the nausea.

The following week Phil was preparing a patient for the same test. She was a middle-aged woman whose depression had been successfully treated with six weeks administration of a tricyclic anti-depressant. After my profound experience of a supercharged serotonin system I was worried she would have an even more powerful reaction because she was on a relatively higher dose of tricyclic than I had taken. But Phil was relaxed, he predicted that the serotonin system that had been so prominently stimulated in me would have been desensitised by the six weeks of tricyclic treatment. Thankfully, he was right. She hardly noticed the l-tryptophan infusion.

So what was different between her and me? Maybe it was that her serotonin system was set lower than mine because she had been depressed? Or was Phil right, the long-term treatment of the tricyclic had altered (we would now say desensitised) the serotonin receptors that were so powerfully stimulated in me. We now know that there are at least 15 different serotonin receptors in our brains and guts and each of these can produce different effects. So, for example the extreme nausea that serotonin stimulation produced in me was due to the activation of 5-HT3 receptors in the nerves in the gut and brain stem that regulate nausea and vomiting. The sleep disruption was due to activation of different subtypes of the 5-HT2 family of receptors, and was an extreme example of what some patients experience early in SSRI treatment when they can have some insomnia and more vivid dreams. The treated depressed patient didn't get any of this because her receptors had been exposed to elevated levels of serotonin for many weeks and so had desensitised.

We now know that these serotonin receptor desensitisations are important in the therapeutic activity of anti-depressants and the fact that they come on over two-to-six weeks of treatment parallels the time course of the improvement in mood. But they don't prove that serotonin levels are low in depressed people or that a serotonin deficit underpins or causes depression or anxiety. So how can we directly test the serotonin causes depression theory?

Way back in the 1950s, soon after serotonin had been discovered in the brain, a group in the UK had measured the concentration of this neurotransmitter in *post-mortem* samples from the brains of people who had died with depression. They found levels were significantly lower than in a control group of brains, suggesting a serotonin deficit caused depression. But such studies are hard to do, there are few brain banks that have 'depressed' brains and also many depressed people are on medications that might alter the serotonin concentrations and its receptors.

By the time we were developing our methods for serotonin stimulation of the brain with l-tryptophan, the new technique of PET scanning had been invented and the first human PET scan was conducted at the MRC Cyclotron Unit at the Hammersmith Hospital (where I still work today). We encouraged the lead chemist there, Vic Pyke, to try to invent tracers for the serotonin system and he then pioneered the development of a tracer that measured the density of the 5-HT1A sub-type of serotonin receptor in the brain. Like most PET tracers this came from a chemical series that a pharmaceutical company had made as possible therapeutics. In the case of this 5-HT1A tracer the compound series was from Wyeth-Ayerst, hence the tracer was called WAY100635 (WAY for short). The series was developed to be a possible new type of anti-depressant that would boost serotonin release by taking off a negative feedback brake that serotonin neurons have. But WAY was never tried as medicine in patients because of toxicity problems when used in pharmacological doses. But when it's used as a tracer then the amounts given are a thousand times lower, and people only have one or two scans, so this use is quite safe.

The reason 5-HT1A receptor acting drugs such as WAY were developed was because there is a high density of these receptors in the parts of the brain that control emotion. Regions such as the hippocampus, amygdala and other parts of the limbic system as well as in the frontal cortical regions. These receptors seemed to be in places where they could mediate the positive effects of serotonin on mood and anxiety. Also, in rodent studies, reducing or blocking these receptors led to depression-like behaviour.

The serotonin PET research team at the MRC Cyclotron Unit led by Paul Grasby and Ilan Rabiner set out to use WAY to ask the question was there a deficit of these receptors in people with depression? They scanned depressed people who were free from any serotonin acting anti-depressants and compared the number of these 5-HT1A receptors with that in an age and gender matched control group. Their results were remarkable — the patients had lower numbers of receptors than the controls, but only in those brain regions involved in depression. The theory was now clear, depression was associated with, and possibly driven by, a relative deficit of serotonin function, i.e. less 5-HT1A receptors meant less serotonin activity in the mood circuit. And SSRIs would lift depression because they increased the amount of serotonin available to the receptors, so offsetting their deficit.

The next question was did the patients' 5-HT1A receptor deficits recover when their mood got better? In technical terms was the low receptor number a state marker (down only when the person was depressed) or was it a trait marker (down even when their mood had lifted)? To resolve this issue Grasby and Rabiner treated their patients with anti-depressants and then scanned them again when they were recovered. Still the receptor number was lower than in the controls, suggesting a low 5-HT1A receptor number was a vulnerability or predisposing factor in depression. Could it even be genetic? This proved harder to test but they did show that non-depressed relatives of the depressed patients also had lower levels of these receptors than the normal controls. This suggests that the low receptor finding is partly genetic and partly environmental.

Faced with these exciting explanatory findings that depression might be associated with a serotonin receptor deficit as shown by the PET scans, and SSRIs worked to offset this and so normalise serotonin underactivity, we asked the question, was the same true for the anxiety disorders? Using the same PET methodology, members of my team, especially John Nash, scanned a number of patients with panic disorder before they started on SSRI treatment. Then we re-scanned the ones who were adequately treated till they came into remission (i.e. were fully-recovered).

At first it seemed that the situation was like in the depressed patients because the panic disorder ones also had low levels of 5-HT1A receptors. But the areas where the deficit was observed were different and the anxiety patients only had lower receptors in the anxiety circuit of the brain. A more surprising finding came when we re-scanned them in recovery, when, unlike in the depressed patients, their receptor number had returned to normal. So, in panic disorder the serotonin receptor deficit was a state marker, related to the illness, not a trait or vulnerability marker as it is in depression.

We still do not know why there was recovery of receptor number in the panic patients but not in the depressed ones. I suspect it's because in the panic group the stress that provokes and perpetuates their anxiety also drives down the receptor number, so when this is removed by the SSRI treatment then the brain can recover to its normal state. In depression the alterations seem more permanent which helps explain why relapse is so common in this disorder. Some other brain imaging studies in families with a strong inherited predisposition to depression suggest that there may even be a structural deficit in those parts of the brain that protect from depression.

Not all depression seems to be caused by the brain having too few 5-HT1A receptors. Other groups have examined the genes that code for the serotonin re-uptake site and found some genetic variants that relate to depression. The most remarkable group of patients are those that have multiple copies of the genes for the serotonin re-uptake site (most of us have just one). The more gene copies there are the more serotonin re-uptake sites are made and so the lower are the levels of serotonin in the synaptic cleft. In other words, people in these families have brains that are chronically deprived of serotonin. We believe that this explains their much-increased risks of depression and other disorders of serotonin such as obsessive compulsive disorder (OCD).

It seems that almost every week I am confronted with patient and lobby groups attacking anti-depressants, claiming that they do more harm than good. Many also refuse to accept that the brain has anything to do with depression and are resistant to the idea that changes in neurotransmitter activity or receptor number might predispose to mood or anxiety disorders. In this chapter I have given a brief overview of why they are wrong. Serotonin is involved in some people's depression or anxiety, and serotonin enhancing medicines like SSRIs are powerful therapeutic agents. Though at present we can't routinely measure serotonin activity in the brain of all our patients, to deny this as a possible theory, and to reject the overwhelming evidence of the efficacy of SSRIs, is an act of faith not of science.

And just last year, almost 70 years since the discovery of serotonin, we became able to answer the key question — is there a deficit of serotonin in the brains of people with depression? In 2019, a young research psychiatrist in our team, David Erritzoe, discovered a way to measure serotonin release in living human brains using PET imaging. He has also shown that depressed people release less serotonin and that the greater their depression the lower their serotonin release! This is the first direct proof in living people of serotonin regulating mood.

CHAPTER 5

Alcohol — A Drug or Not a Drug?

The early days of Tony Blair's New Labour government were a period of some hope for us in the drug and alcohol field. He started by making all the right noises, e.g. experts will decide on policy and alcohol and tobacco will be covered along with other so called 'illegal' drugs. Even more remarkably was the suggestion that they would honour the recommendations of the then recent House of Lords report on cannabis and encourage medical use.

As part of this spirit of openness, a Cabinet Office review of drugs — including alcohol and tobacco — was set up in the late-1990s. I was asked to join and travelled up from Bristol to London on an early morning train every other week (and at my own expense) to join a group of other experts meeting in the basement rooms of Admiralty Arch. There we worked on the data collection and report writing. After nearly a year the report was drafted to the satisfaction of all the 30 or so members. It made a series of sensible recommendations, especially around harm reduction for opioid use. It also pointed out the huge health and social burden of alcohol-related problems and recommended addressing these through pricing and availability measures. As this was the first time any government committee had been allowed to comment on the harms of alcohol in the same context as other drugs we were naturally pleased. It seemed like a watershed moment, the acceptance by government that the legal/illegal distinction was not scientifically valid, all drugs were drugs, and harm reduction was a common way forward.

You can imagine our horror when the final report was published and we discovered that the alcohol chapter had been removed! When we complained to the Cabinet Office they told us that they had run the report by the representatives of the drinks industry who had informed them that our analysis of the harms of alcohol was not correct. Yes, it did lead to deaths from liver disease, hypertension, stroke, cancers, etc. but it also had a protective effect against heart attacks particularly in middle-aged men. This small benefit was sufficient justification for them to reject our recommendations for more controls on alcohol and to unilaterally delete the chapter.

This block on the telling of the truth about alcohol was not just due to the alcohol industry's lobbying. At the time Blair was reported to be in cahoots with Bernie Ecclestone, the head of Formula One motor sport to gain support for New Labour and was dragging his feet over the banning of alcohol advertising in F1 which he managed to delay in return for a significant contribution to New Labour funds. The government tried to appease the academic and health communities by setting up a working committee to oversee alcohol policy. It seemed that they had seen the error of their ways and wanted to make amends. But when the terms of reference of the group were announced we discovered that *half* the seats were to be given to the alcohol industry. Truly a case of the offenders making the laws. The academic/health community members resigned en masse and since then alcohol policy has been in limbo, with both sides lobbying government but the alcohol industry usually winning. For example, alcohol is still advertised on TV and in cinemas whereas similar cigarette advertising is banned.

Also, grudgingly, following pressure from health groups, a decision was made to insist that all alcoholic drinks should have health warnings like on cigarette packets, but this has still not happened. Because this failure represents a serious breach of regulations and one which could lead to serious health harms, e.g. in terms of foetal alcohol syndrome we are now considering taking the industry to judicial review over it. In the succeeding decade the one concession by the alcohol industry has been to add the words 'Please use responsibly' to bottles and adverts. This is truly a platitude since the main reason many people drink alcohol, especially the young, is to lose responsibility.

The impact of this decision to cave-in to alcohol industry pressure has been revealed over the subsequent 15 years or so which have seen alcohol become the leading cause of death in men under 50 in the UK. The increased level of alcohol consumption in women seen in recent years and driven by their increasing incomes and independence means we can expect this frightening statistic to apply to women under the age of 50 in just a few years' time. In the last year for which data is available (2018) young women's drinking exceeded that of men for the first time ever, as they are now earning on average more than men of their own age. And alcohol is a key element of the social life of many working women.

The health harms of alcohol have become more and more apparent over this time. We now know it is implicated in at least eight cancers and may be the only, as yet, known preventable cause of breast cancer. It also makes a significant contribution to dementias with recent data suggesting up to 20 per cent of early onset cases are due to alcohol-induced brain damage. As well as causing liver injury, alcohol is the leading cause of hypertension that leads to heart attacks and strokes; in fact alcohol kills more people from these complications than from liver cirrhosis. Friday and Saturday nights find most hospital casualty departments overflowing with people injured whilst drunk, or just drunk and incapable. Overall, the cost of alcohol use to the NHS is estimated at over £3.5 billion per year.

The impact on non-drinkers is also profound. Public drunkenness and alcohol-inspired violence at weekends make many of our inner cities no-go areas for the general public. Policing this weekly public order chaos costs the UK over £6.5 billion per year! As well as through road traffic accidents that harm innocent drivers or pedestrians, alcohol also has a hugely damaging impact on family life. Most cases of domestic violence occur when the perpetrator is drunk, and the psychological damage caused by a repeatedly drunken parent can scar children for life.

Even worse, children are damaged by alcohol even before they are born. Excessive alcohol consumption in the mother can lead to foetal damage — foetal alcohol syndrome. This is a form of brain damage that affects all aspects of the child's development often leaving him or her severely intellectually and behaviourally disturbed. Many are extremely hyperactive and spend their whole lives in institutional care. We estimate that the number of children damaged by alcohol in utero is more than the total of all children born with Down's syndrome, autism and fragile X syndrome together. Foetal alcohol syndrome is by far the leading cause of childhood intellectual disability in the UK.

This constellation of harms that alcohol produces in non-drinkers is the reason why, in our 2010 *Lancet* paper on drug harms in the UK, alcohol came out as the worst harm. It is not the most harmful drug to the user, heroin, crack and crystal (methamphetamine) do more damage to the person taking them.

But because of the wide use of alcohol in the population — around 85 per cent of adults under 60 drink — it has by far the biggest negative impact on society. Why do we as a society put up with this? There are many contributory answers to this question. Alcohol is a product of fruit degradation so has always been with us. The deliberate fermenting of grain to make beer has existed as long as written history, with the first evidence of brewing being found in China over 6,000 years ago. It's possible fermenting honey into mead was invented over 40,000 years before that in Africa. Humans like to drink alcohol — and in many cases to get drunk. Alcohol relaxes them and breaks down social inhibitions which is why it is a vital ingredient in a 'good party.' It also reduces anxiety which is why the first thing that happens when the seat belt sign is switched off on an airplane is that alcohol is offered to passengers. Many people are a little anxious about flying and alcohol eases this worry.

Many people turn to alcohol to overcome anxiety in other situations such as work pressure or trauma. Here its effects tend to decrease over time, a phenomenon we call tolerance. This leads to increased consumption and eventually in many people to dependence on it. A good example of this is Frida Kahlo the great Mexican painter. When her husband the muralist Ribera started having affairs she turned to alcohol to comfort her and said later 'I tried to drown my sorrows in drink, but they learned how to swim.' Countless other famous artists and performers have gone down the same path. In the present time I have observed both Anthony McPartlin (of 'Ant and Dec' TV presenting fame) and the Swedish disc jockey, Avicii, have had their careers adversely affected by alcohol (and in Avicii's case his life ended).

On a brighter note Eminem has just celebrated his tenth year of being abstinent. It's a great sadness that another star, musician Amy Winehouse couldn't crack her alcohol habit and died when she reportedly relapsed to drinking after a period of abstinence. The amount of alcohol she drank would not have killed her when she was drinking heavily as she would have been tolerant to its actions. But during her six weeks period of abstinence this tolerance would have been lost so that when she relapsed and drank her reported usual amount (a litre of vodka a day) she unfortunately died.

In the UK three young people a week die as a result of alcohol poisoning. This is often on their birthdays when their friends and family think it's fun to get them drunk, and then are mortified when they never recover. Alcohol plays an important part of all celebrations, from toasting the new baby to sending off the deceased grandparent, but birthdays are the most dangerous time. A few years ago, I tried to find an eighteenth birthday card for a nephew of mine that didn't celebrate alcohol and drunkenness. I had to discard 22 consecutive cards before I found an alcohol-free one.

I suspect that most people in the UK are not aware of the true scale of alcohol harms so don't argue for a reduction in drinking. And the drinks industry's media machine is determined to keep it that way. This industry spends about 1,000 times more on advertising persuading us to drink than the Department of Health spends on warning us of the harms of alcohol. The power of the alcohol lobby to government, with the possible exception of the weapons industry, is the most effective of all lobbyists. Proof of its power is that it has managed to prevent successive governments banning alcohol advertising when the tobacco industry couldn't stop the ban on cigarette advertising. I estimate that about half of all UK members of Parliament get some benefit from the drinks industry in the forms of free drinks, free hospitality and free 'fact finding' overseas trips. No wonder they won't vote to change the liberal licensing laws that have encouraged the rise and rise of alcohol to become the leading cause of death in young people in the UK.

In real terms alcohol is now about three times more affordable than it was 50 years ago. It's also available in supermarkets and even 24/7 in many corner shops, whereas it used only to be available during licensing hours in pubs and off-licences. This price reduction and increased availability means that today the average UK person drinks about eleven litres of alcohol per year compared to about six litres in 1970. This doubling of consumption has had such a big impact on health because the relationship between alcohol intake and harms is not a straight line — it's exponential. Someone drinking ten units of alcohol a day (about a bottle and a third of wine) will have over eight times the harms from alcohol of someone drinking half that amount. This means that reductions in consumption from high intakes have a proportionally greater health impact than reductions from lower levels of intake.

It is this intensified improvement effect of high-end reduction that led the Scottish government to push for minimum unit pricing of alcohol. Scotland suffers disproportionately more alcohol-related damage than the rest of the UK. It has higher levels of binge-drinking and cirrhosis and at any one time about

30 per cent of all the intensive care beds in the country are occupied by people with an alcohol-related illness. Following advice from a range of health experts the Scottish government decided to use the minimum unit pricing approach. This sets the lowest price that a unit (eight gm, or 10ml (2020)) of alcohol can be sold for. Currently (2020) there is no wider minimum which explains why supermarkets in England and Wales can use alcohol as a 'loss leader' selling it at less than the price of some bottled waters. There are examples of a two litre bottle of strong (eight per cent) cider being sold for about £2. This bottle contains 20 units of alcohol — the maximum recommended limit for men per week. Often several of these bottles are drunk each day by an individual because they are so cheap, and the users are so tolerant.

The Scottish experts argued that a minimum unit price of 50 pence per unit would reduce alcohol consumption by about ten per cent. This doesn't seem a lot, but because of the exponential curve of consumption versus harm this is predicted to reduce harms by about 30 per cent. Moreover, the main effect would be in those severely affected by alcohol and the young, the two most vulnerable groups. In reality, few drinkers currently consume alcohol that costs less than 50 pence per unit. The average bottle of wine costs about £6 (in a supermarket) which equates to about 66 pence per unit. Minimum unit pricing would have had almost no impact on the profits of the drinks industry but still the industry fought back viciously. They contested the decision in the Scottish courts — and lost. The alcohol industry then took it to European Court of Justice — and lost.

Worryingly this last defeat, however, gave the drinks industry a glimmer of hope, a possible escape clause because the court said that minimum unit pricing was acceptable under European law provided that there were no more efficient means of achieving the same health goals. So, the drinks industry went back to the Scottish courts and argued that minimum unit pricing wasn't proven to deliver the health benefits claimed. After a tense hearing they lost again. They then played their last appeal card — to the UK Supreme Court where they lost yet again. It is now in law in Scotland. So after seven years of fighting the Scottish government brought in 50 pence per unit minimum pricing. Already we have seen a reduction in consumption and hospital admissions and over the next few years I predict we shall see significant impacts on health and other alcohol-related problems.

This saga reflects the lengths to which the drinks industry will go to avoid any change in the status quo. Even though minimum unit pricing would not have impacted their profits (indeed it might make them grow) they wanted to prove that they were in control of decision-making on alcoholic products. They used the Scottish whisky industry as the front organization to argue against the change because they thought this group would have maximum public leverage, whisky being a key local product (and despite no quality whiskies being sold at less than the minimum unit price). These apparent shortcomings in the integrity of the Whisky Association were exposed by another local alcohol producer, Tennent's, who broke ranks and gave public support for the government's action for the benefit of the nation. This was a strong statement because they had been the source of one of the worst offenders in terms of strong cheap lagers — Tennent's Super Strength nine per cent lager was commonly sold at about 30 pence a unit.

CHAPTER 6

Ecstasy or Not?

My first encounter with the Home Office drugs section came when I was invited to join a working group on ecstasy deaths. The meeting was convened by my old boss from Oxford, David Grahame-Smith, who was Chair of the Advisory Council on the Misuse of Drugs (ACMD) at that time. There had been several high-profile reports of young people dying in all-night dance clubs associated with ecstasy use. We examined the evidence and found that most cases were due to extreme elevations in body temperature (hyperthermia). But questions remained, was this caused by the chemicals in ecstasy or by the excessive dancing, or some combination of the two? And what could we do about it?

We knew that the ecstasy being used at that time was largely a relatively pure form of the chemical MDMA. This was an old drug that had been made in the early-1900s as a possible blood-clotting agent but soon discarded. It was then resurrected in the 1950s for possible psychoactive effects as one of many compounds made by the US chemist Alexander ('Sasha') Shulgin as reference standards for the US Federal Drug Enforcement Administration (DEA) (often called 'Agency'). As a true human scientific psychopharmacologist he tested all those drugs he synthesised on himself. This meant that, over time, he became probably the most experienced drug self-experimentalist in human history, especially in relation to stimulant-type drugs.

Alexander Shulgin and Ann Shulgin (his wife) described this self-research in their groundbreaking book, *PiHKAL: A Chemical Love Story* ('PhHKAL' standing for Phenylethylamines I have Known and Loved) (1991, Transform Press). With his wide experience of different stimulants, Shulgin realised that MDMA was a quite unique drug. He commented on its special effects: clarity of feeling, increased empathy and positive emotions towards others. These properties led to him getting Ann to share the drug experience with him and she confirmed its remarkable, positive effects and saw potential therapeutic benefits in it.

Ann was a (lay, i.e. unqualified) psychotherapist but saw at once how this drug could have huge potential to help couples overcome the irritations and dissatisfactions with each other that build up over decades of living together. Under her guidance MDMA was then introduced into the community of US West Coast psychotherapists especially for couples' therapy in doses of around 10mg per person. It became popular amongst marital therapists in California, led by Leo Zeff. It was taken during a psychotherapy session to help couples rediscover their previous affections for each other. MDMA, we now know, releases serotonin in the brain and this can produce strongly positive feelings of empathy and mood towards others. These positive feelings are often strong enough to overcome the irritations and niggles, dissatisfaction and dishar-mony already mentioned. In simple terms MDMA puts the love back into a marriage — couples rediscover their early affection for each other and are then prepared to work together to restore this state.

In these US couples' therapeutic sessions there were few if any adverse effects of MDMA, so what was happening in the clubs and at raves? It turned out that the deaths were related to two factors — hyperthermia and dehydration — and not to impurities in the ecstasy which at that time was largely pure MDMA. The hyperthermia we thought was in part due to the release of serotonin by MDMA since this was well-established in animal models, something I had explored in my doctorate research. But we felt this rise in body temperature was being exacerbated by the prolonged dancing that many 'clubbers' were engag-ing in. This persistent and at times extreme dancing would itself increase body temperature but also lead to sweating and then dehydration. A vicious cycle would then develop with dehydration worsening the hyperthermia because, in order to keep blood pressure stable, the body shuts down blood flow in the skin. This then reduces sweating so a cycle of increasing body temperature begins.

It turned out that some clubs were making the dehydration situation worse in several ways. Some were trying to encourage people to drink alcohol by shutting off the water taps in the toilets, and most had poor ventilation so that the clubs became excessively hot particularly when large numbers were danc-ing (this might also have been a ploy to get people to spend more on drinks).

Our committee took the view that a harm reduction approach was required. Prohibition hadn't worked, MDMA had been banned several years before and yet was still being as widely used as ever, up to a million doses per weekend, and there was little evidence of harm outside of these rare and potentially avoidable deaths. We recommended to the Home Office and Department of Health that they insist clubs make water freely available, in the bar as well as in their toilets. We also asked them to encourage local authorities to remove licences from clubs that did not install 'chill-out' rooms where clubbers could cool down after dancing. In addition, we initiated a public education campaign to warn ecstasy users of the dangers of overheating and dehydration.

These harm reduction approaches proved exceptionally successful and in the past 20 years there have been very few deaths from either dehydration or hyperthermia when people have used sensible doses of MDMA, i.e. less than 125mg per night.

Perverse effects of precursor bans

Ecstasy-related deaths still do occur, but these have different causes. Some are due to the replacement of MDMA with para-Methoxyamphetamine (PMA) and related more toxic stimulants, some are due to the then current rise in the strength of MDMA in ecstasy tablets and crystals, and some due to water retention as in the case of Leah Betts (discussed later in this chapter).

The first two can be attributed to the attempt in the 1990s by the United Nations to eliminate the production of MDMA by banning its precursor safrole. The banning of MDMA under the UN Conventions had not stopped its widespread use which irritated the UN. So, they sought to reduce MDMA production by banning safrole, which is an oil extracted from the sassafras plant. This ban allowed national police forces to make seizures of safrole under UN regulations and in 2005 in Thailand a massive safrole seizure was made. It amounted to 50 tons, which at the time was enough to make half the world's annual supply of MDMA. The UN celebrated this seeming success believing incorrectly that with the precursor no longer available MDMA couldn't be made.

But the black market doesn't work like that. The Chinese underground chemists denied their safrole didn't just give up saying, 'It's a fair cop, I'll make some antibiotics instead.' No, with an order waiting and some serious threat of harm hanging over them for non-delivery, they desperately searched around for alternatives to safrole that might be turned into chemicals that could be sold on as MDMA. The easiest alternative to get hold of was aniseed oil (anethole) which is a widely used base for cosmetics, perfumes or food flavourings and so could never be banned.

When anethole is put through the same chemistry that turns safrole into MDMA the final product is either PMA or PMMA (paramethoxymetham-phetamine). These are two powerful stimulants that were banned under the 1971 UN Conventions on synthetic drugs. Until the 2005 safrole seizure there had been almost no deaths from these in the previous 30 years. Suddenly ecstasy users started dying and at *post-mortems* were found to have PMA or PMMA in their blood but not MDMA. For a few years in the later-2000s the majority of so-called ecstasy deaths in the UK were actually caused by PMA or PMMA. These two synthetic stimulant drugs are more dangerous than MDMA in two ways. First, they are absorbed more slowly by the gut so when a person takes them expecting the usual 'come up' from MDMA within 30 minutes it doesn't happen. They then think they have been sold a weak lot of ecstasy tabs so take a couple more to try to take an effective dose. But by then it's too late—they have overdosed! Within an hour the PMA/PMMA has got into their brain and started to release serotonin. And these drugs also block the enzyme monoam-ine oxidase responsible for breaking-down serotonin. In effect PMA/PMMA leads to a state of serotonin poisoning called the serotonin syndrome (which is more usually seen when a serotonin enhancer, e.g. paroxetine is given with a monoamine oxidase blocker such as phenelzine). This syndrome can be lethal through elevating body temperature excessively.

What was especially sad about these deaths is that most would have been prevented if the UK government had done what the Dutch and other more progressive legislatures did—allowed tablet testing and warned people of PMA/PMMA tabs being in circulation. For unfathomable reasons, the UK Home Office refuses to share its information about false, more toxic, ecstasy pills. One batch—the Superman pills—killed three people in the UK despite hav-ing been detected weeks before in The Netherlands. The UK government was told of these new dangerous pills being in circulation but claimed, disingenuously, given the wide reach of the BBC and social media, that they had no way of warning the public!

Fortunately, PMA/PMMA deaths are on the decline but MDMA deaths are now rising. This is because the Thai safrole seizure forced MDMA makers to seek sources of safrole other than the sassafras plant. New synthetic routes were determined and now there is a glut of safrole in the world. So MDMA became easier to make than ever and therefore cheaper than it was. This glut of MDMA has led to the amounts of MDMA in pills increasing from 50mg 20 years ago to 150mg or even 250mg now. Worse, MDMA in crystalline form is now being made and sold in one gram quantities, and a bag of this size can be lethal if taken by one person in one evening session.

Overall the UN attack on MDMA has caused more harm than good, just like most of the battles in the UN's war on drugs have done. The banning of MDMA had little medical justification and was mostly a moral crusade against a new way for young people to have fun. In most countries (including the UK and US) MDMA was put into the highest (supposedly most harmful) class of controlled drugs, so attracting the most severe penalties. This makes it a Class A drug alongside heroin and cocaine, which on any measure are much more harmful drugs.

In the US MDMA was in Schedule 1 but with the bizarre argument that it was both a psychedelic and a stimulant so the penalties for possession or supply were the total of those for both sorts of drug. In other words, in US sentencing policy MDMA was treated as if it was a combination of LSD and cocaine. Penalties for possessing even a few dozen pills could be up to 20 years in prison. One of the greatest achievements of Drug Science so far has been to work with the American Civil Liberties Union and challenge this decision in a court in New York. When Val Curran presented the data on the true relative harms of MDMA compared with psychedelics and cocaine the judge was outraged at the dishonesty of the scientists who had championed the dual counting of harms. He dramatically reduced the prison terms for MDMA to less than a quarter of what they had been.

The ecstasy story is a fascinating pastiche of political disinformation about the real harms of a drug being bolstered by supposed scientific research. The banning of MDMA was a political act driven by the media who created a moral panic about its use, particularly during raves. The rave problem was of little concern to the police who when monitoring ecstasy users found themselves, for the first time in their police careers, being treated with love and affection. This contrasted so clearly with the violence and abuse they often received from the alcohol-intoxicated people they were usually sent to police, meaning that they were most happy to be asked to monitor raves.

So, if the police weren't arguing for a ban on ecstasy who was? One possibility is the alcohol industry. The period during which we saw the rise of the rave scene was the only time in the past 50 years when alcohol sales stopped their relentless year-on-year rise. But on what grounds could the government intervene? The answer was health harms. But these were relatively minor and could be minimised by harm reduction measures, so then they fell back on the tried and trusted 'precautionary' principle. Maybe ecstasy use would over months or years lead to brain damage? This fear was then developed into a fact by a series of poorly designed and over-interpreted studies that anti-ecstasy crusaders used to justify the government's decisions on banning it, and heavy penalties for possession or sale.

Then there was the tragic death of Leah Betts, unquestionably the most high-profile UK ecstasy death ever. Leah was a normal, happy teenager who for reasons that are unclear, but probably reflect a desire to have a special celebration, took two ecstasy tablets on her eighteenth birthday while she and a friend were preparing her parents' house for her party. We estimate the dose she took was probably two 40mg of MDMA, i.e. 80mg, exactly the dose we used in our subsequent Channel 4 funded brain imaging study of MDMA (see *Chapter 15*), and which we found perfectly safe, even in middle-aged people.

So why did Leah sadly die? The details of that afternoon are not exactly clear but it appears that as she experienced the 'come up' from the MDMA she seems to have begun to worry that she was suffering from the well-reported ecstasy dehydration syndrome. So, she started to drink water to combat it. But she wasn't dancing and sweating off water, she was simply making her house ready for the party. During the course of the afternoon, Leah is reputed to have drunk seven litres of water which put her into coma with 'water poisoning.' So much water would do that to most of us. In the UK each year there are around ten deaths from excessive water intake (polydypsia) and after a couple of days in intensive care Leah unfortunately died from the consequences of brain swelling from the excessive water.

If Leah had been better informed about what to do to minimise the risks of MDMA, e.g. only drinking when dancing a lot, it seems likely that she would not have drunk so much water and would still be alive today. However, we can't be sure about this, for in those days we were less aware of the risks of excessive water intake in people who had taken MDMA. We now know that MDMA can release a hormone that helps the body retain water (anti-diuretic hormone or ADH). This effect is most pronounced in young women and can lead to water poisoning even if they don't drink as much as Leah did. It seems this susceptibility of young women to the ADH releasing effects of ecstasy is now the main factor in MDMA causing harm, and young , for reasons we don't yet understand, are most vulnerable, especially if they take high doses of the drug.

Leah's death became a *cause célèbre*. This was partly because her parents were anti-drug educationalists. It's bad enough to lose a child but to lose a daughter to the very behaviour they had been seeking to prevent must have been doubly heartbreaking. Leah's parents initiated a campaign that led to MDMA being vilified even more than it had been already, to scare users away. They gained an audience with the Prime Minister of the time, Tony Blair, who promised he would never re-schedule MDMA despite the limited evidence of harm.

Across the UK Leah's face appeared on billboards to warn people of the harms of ecstasy in a multi-million pound advertising campaign about this drug's harms, the like of which has never been seen before or since. Who paid for this? It certainly wasn't the government and the evidence points to the drinks industry, for soon after this campaign it seems the agency that ran it gained a massive contract from one of the world's biggest producers of alcoholic spirits and beers. The rise of ecstasy and the rave culture was the first major threat to the profitability of the alcohol industry since prohibition. For the first time in decades they saw their sales beginning to fall as young people switched to MDMA. Something had to be done and Leah's death somehow became the springboard to scare people off ecstasy.

Of course, the industry did, and continues to do, other things. One famous advert that was soon banned was for Bacardi, depicting a psychedelic dancing cat. They also began to induce younger and younger people to use alcohol by making sweet-tasting drinks such as alcopops and breezers, in the hope that by the time they encountered ecstasy they would already have an alcohol habit. And they undermined the bans on advertising to young people using new outlets such as social media and sports clubs. To a large extent the drinks industry won the battle, and the rave-induced dent in sales was turned around as ecstasy and raves were banned. Alcohol consumption rose again year-on-year and a new peak of intake was achieved in the 2010s which explains why alcohol is now the leading cause of death in men under 50 in the UK today (and as already noted women are now drinking as much as men; they will soon reach this unwelcome statistic too).

The so-called science around ecstasy is some of the most questionable ever in my view. Animal studies of its toxicity were conducted using doses well above those that human users would. In the most celebrated case, the group of George Ricaurte in John Hopkins University, US claimed to have found that ecstasy given along with loud music (to mimic a rave) caused irreversible brain damage in monkeys. This paper was published in the supposedly 'leading' scientific journal *Science*, despite referees saying it was probably in error. *Science* is the main journal of the American Association of Science, a professional organization which gets significant funding from the US government. It is reputed that the journal's editor was 'encouraged' to publish the paper by powerful senators even though the peer-reviewers believed its data were wrong. These senators wanted to send a clear message that MDMA use was illegal because it was harmful.

Because the paper was published in such a high-profile journal it attracted so much scientific attention and criticism that the researchers were forced to go back and verify their results. When they did this they found, to their horror, but as predicted by their critics, that the experiment had gone very, very wrong. Instead of giving the monkeys MDMA they had instead used methamphetamine (crystal meth). This is significantly more potent and so more toxic than MDMA which explains why the monkeys got brain damage. The paper was retracted but with much less media attention than its publication had received, so many still believe its retracted findings to be true. As one of the authors of that paper reputedly said, even if the science was wrong MDMA still wasn't a safe drug so we should dissuade people from using it. Since then much better-conducted studies in monkeys of MDMA at human-relevant doses have been conducted and no evidence for brain damage has been produced.

This attitude, that it is a self-evident fact that MDMA is dangerous, so all 'scientists' have to do is find evidence to prove this fact, permeates much research around this drug. Scientific methodology is ignored to facilitate findings of 'significant harm.' The same group who undertook the methamphetamine instead of MDMA monkey study also conducted a study on the effects of MDMA use on sleep and claimed that users had more disrupted sleep than non-users. As serotonin is a major neurotransmitter involved in sleep; they argued this was evidence for ecstasy-induced damage to the serotonin system in the brain. We decided to try to replicate their study which we felt was confounded by the fact that they had flown in ecstasy-users from all over the US and hadn't allowed adequate time for them to overcome their jet-lag. In addition, we decided to stress the serotonin system to magnify any possible deficits in serotonin function. We did this using the well-established technique of tryptophan depletion which has been proved to reduce serotonin activity in the brain. Tryptophan depletion given before sleep at night reliably enhances REM (dreaming) sleep because serotonin is required to suppress REM. This is probably the most sensitive measure of serotonin function in the brain.

Robin Carhart-Harris (then a PhD student) and Sue Wilson (our sleep EEG expert) conducted the study by comparing a group of ecstasy users with a control group matched for age gender, etc. They found, as predicted, tryptophan depletion did enhance REM sleep, but the effect was identical in both groups. Moreover, the ecstasy users' sleep was not abnormal in any way. To our minds this was clear proof that ecstasy use didn't damage the serotonin system — at least in relation to one of its key functions, sleep.

Because sleep is the brain function most sensitive to serotonin depletion we believe that our study provided the best evidence yet that ecstasy use does not permanently damage the serotonin system in the brain. So, we submitted our results to the same journal that had published the John Hopkins ecstasy-users sleep study and within two days received a disturbing reply from the editor. He said that we had better send it to another, non-American, journal because it would be impossible to publish a negative finding for MDMA on brain serotonin in a US journal! We were shocked but not surprised; his honesty meant that we didn't waste months or years having US referees try to block our publication. The truth is that the US drug research funding system through the National Institute of Drug Abuse predicates that only studies that will (or are likely to) find evidence of harm from illegal drugs can be funded. This is one of the most blatant examples of how the drug laws that control recreational drugs fundamentally impede science and scientists.

Many of the other studies purporting to show brain damage from MDMA suffer from the same problems of overstating the significance of the results and extreme extrapolations of possible future harms. A brain imaging study of the serotonin system claimed MDMA damage even though the values of the MDMA users were all in the normal range. One study of memory changes over five years during which time MDMA had been used found a tiny clinically-irrelevant reduction that was then proclaimed as proving ecstasy did cause brain damage. The other data in the paper that showed MDMA users performed better than the controls on other tasks was conveniently ignored.

It was because of this systematic vilification of MDMA as a toxic dangerous substance that I began to explore the question of relative harms of different drugs, and also the more politically controversial issue of what is the threshold of harm above which it is proportionate to make a drug a controlled drug. It seemed to me that at the least there should be evidence of significant harm, but how much? And what are the appropriate comparators? We ban guns because of their dangers, but we don't ban motorcycles even though many more people die from riding these than from ecstasy (300 versus 30 per year respectively). Or horse riding where deaths and serious injury are surprisingly common.

In my most controversial paper ('Equasy—An Overlooked Addiction with Implications for Drug Policy' (2009, *Journal of Psychopharmacology,* 23: 3–5)), I treated horse-riding as if it were a drug, renaming it Equasy (equine addiction syndrome) and then compared its harms across different parameters such as death, injury, social harms, addictiveness, etc. From this analysis I estimated that death or serious injury was more likely from riding (particularly over jumps) than from taking an ecstasy tablet. This observation invoked enormous anger from politicians, sections of the right-wing media and the horse-riding community. I was accused by the then Home Secretary, Jacqui Smith of exceeding my remit as the government's lead drugs advisor. She said my paper was an insult to families whose loved ones had died from horse riding because it associated a legal activity with an illegal one. I pointed out that as a scientist I had to make such comparisons in order to determine if a drug was sufficiently harmful to be made illegal, to which she replied with a phrase that has become etched in my memory: 'You can't compare a legal activity with an illegal one!'

At that moment, in the phone conversation with the Home Secretary, I thought that she was speaking just for herself. Later as I shared her assertion with other politicians, particularly Evan Harris, one of the few medically-qualified MPs, it began to become clear that the majority of them believed the same—once illegal, always illegal. It was at that point I realised what I, and the whole scientific community, were up against in relation to the drug laws—politicians could not think rationally about anything that was illegal. This insight made me realise just how important it therefore was to ensure that other drugs, where levels of harm are uncertain or low, should not be made illegal for this decision could never be overturned. There could never be a reasoned debate about relative harms which is why *no* drug has ever been taken out of the Misuse of Drugs Act 1971 (MDA 1971) in the 50 years since it was brought into law.

I suppose we should never have expected Jacqui Smith to engage candidly with the review process. Previous Home Secretaries had refused the ACMD permission to review the status of ecstasy, in case they came to the view it was classified too highly. This decision would have put them in direct conflict with Tony Blair who had (without talking to the ACMD or other experts) personally promised the family of Leah Betts that he would *never* downgrade it. Our opportunity to review the status of MDMA under the MDA 1971 only came following the Science and Technology Select Committee review of evidence-based policy. Gordon Brown launched his premiership with the promise that his would be the most evidence-based government in history. Two years later the Science and Technology Select Committee, under the leadership of Phil Willis, a senior Liberal Democrat, decided they would see if his promise would be kept. They decided to review four areas of policy, health, finance, education and drugs, so Mike Rawlins (the ACMD Chair at the time) and I (as Chair of the ACMD Technical Committee) were called to give oral evidence alongside the current Drugs Minister.

In general, the Select Committee found that the ACMD had worked well and the government had heeded our suggestions to some extent. But they were surprised that the regulatory status of MDMA hadn't ever been the subject of an ACMD review and asked us why. We replied that the Home Office had refused us permission. So, they turned to the Drugs Minister, Vernon Coaker, and asked him why this was so. He replied that whatever the ACMD review came up with they would never downgrade ecstasy. The committee then asked him if he understood the nature of evidence and Vernon gave his now famous reply, 'Of course we do! Evidence is what we seek to justify our policy decisions.' The whole hearing burst out laughing; clearly in drug policy, the cart was still before the horse!

Pleasingly the committee insisted that a review take place and the Home Secretary (Jacqui Smith) was asked about her views on this and replied it was 'unwelcome,' further setting the scene for a showdown if the status quo was to be challenged. And challenged it was. Our report confirmed what most knowledgeable people already knew, MDMA was inappropriately classified. By that time, I had succeeded Rawlins as Chair of the ACMD so the hearing and report writing fell to me. Being aware of the challenges over the two prior reviews of cannabis (which are detailed in *Chapter 7*) and the argument that open voting might have put pressure on some to go along with the group's opinion, I decided to instigate a secret ballot over the preferred status of MDMA. As Chair, and so holding the casting vote, I didn't vote at this stage nor express an opinion. In the end all but two of the 26 members voted to downgrade MDMA to Class B and one voted for Class C. We therefore recommended MDMA be made a Class B drug alongside other amphetamines.

The government didn't agree, even after I tried to make sense of the comparative safety of ecstasy by comparing it with a love of horse riding; and, so, my first falling out with the government occurred. I received a warning letter from the Home Secretary, something I learnt much later was in fact the first of my two yellow cards! Still, censure from the Home Office wasn't going to stop me and I continued to argue for rational science-based drug policy.

CHAPTER 7

Conflicts Over Cannabis

The Runciman Committee — Drawing the Battle Lines

In the late-1990s, I was invited to join the Runciman review of the drug laws. This was a committee of experts set up and chaired by Viscountess Ruth Runciman and funded by the Police Foundation. This is a charity that sponsors research into the philosophy and value of policing and is not to be confused with the Police Federation which is the police 'trade union' (other than for the most senior ranks). Ruth had until recently been a leading member of the ACMD, and one of the driving forces behind the introduction of needle exchanges into the UK under the Thatcher government. This was at the time a controversial plan to reduce the spread of AIDS, and one that Margaret Thatcher, Prime Minister, opposed politically. But the 'Iron Lady' allowed it because she believed in the scientific approach to harm reduction — at least for HIV. It was an outstanding success and the UK became a world leader in HIV harm reduction with one of the lowest infection rates in IV drug users in the world. Ruth was therefore an ideal person to take on the challenge of reviewing the drug laws nearly 30 years after they had been codified in the 1971 Misuse of Drugs Act (MDA 1971).

It was a remarkable committee with several impressive individuals. Bernard Williams the philosopher and Simon Jenkins the writer and journalist were challenging and thought-provoking individuals who were prepared to disembowel any half-thought-through ideas or suggestions. Rudi Fortson, one of the leading drugs lawyers in the UK, helped us make sense of the 1971 Act and Ruth herself provided the wisdom and guidance to bring together what was generally received as a major piece of work. In it I developed my first approach to comparing the relative harm of drugs using a nine-point scale — more of which later.

When the report was published most of our many suggestions were accepted by the public and media as being sensible and evidence-based. To our amazement a number of newspapers that were usually anti-drug reform such as the *Daily Mail* and *Daily Telegraph* criticised us for not going far enough. At the time we thought that we had won the arguments and policy change would follow inexorably. For a while it seemed as if we were right. The Home Secretary at the time, David Blunkett saw our arguments for reducing the classification of cannabis from A or B (where different formulations of cannabis were located at the time) to C and asked the ACMD to formally review its status under the MDA 1971.

In 2003 the ACMD — of which by then I was a member — confirmed the Runciman analysis and recommended that all forms of cannabis should be Class C. The government agreed and a decision was made to re-classify cannabis at the end of January 2004. For reasons that I still do not understand, but presumably reflect several years of behind-the-scenes lobbying, and a change of heart from their owners and editors, those newspapers that in 2000 had said we were being too conservative suddenly turned and attacked the government and the ACMD for being too progressive. A massive campaign to block the re-classification of cannabis took place. This failed and cannabis was downgraded but with the proviso that the penalties for supply/dealing be pushed up from seven to 14 years (the same as for Class B drugs).

But the attacks on cannabis continued. Blunkett was replaced as Home Secretary by Charles Clarke, who we first came across in *Chapter 1* as the president of the Cambridge Students' Union in 1972. Now, in 2005, he was a senior member of Blair's cabinet, and one of the few prepared to speak his mind and oppose Blair on issues in public (a behaviour that eventually got him sacked). Clarke asked the ACMD to review the status of cannabis again, in case we had got it wrong on the first analysis! The second review was led, as was the first one, by Mike Rawlins, ex-head of the Committee on Safety of Medicines, one of the leading clinical pharmacologists in the UK. We took evidence from many stakeholders in a series of open meetings then discussed this in closed sessions to produce a report and a recommendation. Although the decision was not unanimous, the vast majority of the committee wanted cannabis to stay in Class C, so we put that to Clarke.

Clarke, the government and the anti-cannabis media were not happy with our recommendations. But he came up with a good compromise. Maybe it was the inflexibility of the MDA 1971 that was the problem? So, he asked the ACMD to begin a review of this Act which by then was over 30-years-old and had never been reviewed. We saw this as a once-in-a-generation opportunity for change and began immediately to survey the different types of rules and regulations used to control drugs in other countries. Unfortunately, soon after this Clarke fell out with Blair and was sacked as Home Secretary on account of a failure to deport foreign criminals when they were discharged from prison. He was replaced by the Scottish ex-ship worker, John Reid, who took the view — in his own words, 'There's nay votes in drugs.' Immediately, and without consulting the ACMD, he scrapped the review process, which has stayed scrapped ever since.

But there were some in government who did believe there were votes in drugs, because a police campaign against cannabis users was prioritised. The police, who at that time were relaxed about cannabis because 'stoners' didn't cause them anything like as much trouble as drunks, were incentivised to catch people in possession of cannabis. Cannabis arrests were made an outcome target for the police and they responded with enthusiasm as this is arguably the easiest crime to detect. All they had to do in their minds was go into a park in London, stop and search a young black man and there was fair chance some remnants of a cannabis spliff would be found.

The number of cannabis arrests soared, and the policy was clearly racist as three to four times more black and ethnic minority people were prosecuted than cannabis use statistics would have predicted. This campaign led to over a million young people — mostly men — being given a criminal record and so created an underclass with severely limited job prospects. It's hard to get into the Civil Service, teaching or other professions with a criminal record. For many people with such convictions, crime — especially drug dealing — was their only hope of employment. This government policy was utterly lacking in intellectual foundation and proportionality; how could a trace of cannabis be a justification for a criminal record? But it went ahead anyway as Blair's New

Labour party tried to curry favour with the right-wing press by being even 'tougher on crime' than the Tories had been.

This policy enraged fair-minded people including many rational police officers who found this target distasteful and dishonest, and one that was having damaging effects on police-community relations. In the end this punitive and unnecessary policing approach was a major factor in precipitating the 2011 riots in London and other UK cities with significant ethnic minority populations. The policy has left a nasty stain on police-public relations that may be hard to erase and also led some police to join a new organization called Law Enforcement Against Prohibition (LEAP) that now campaigns against irrational and counterproductive drugs laws in many countries.

The anti-cannabis rhetoric didn't stop with an assault on recreational users, it continued against those using medical cannabis too. Cannabis had been a medicine in the UK until 1971 when it was removed from the pharmacopeia under the MDA 1971. This was the result of persistent pressure from the US which had removed it from their pharmacopeia several decades before in the bizarre belief that this would reduce recreational use. Despite evidence to the contrary, the US pressurised the UK government on a regular basis to get us to ban medical cannabis too and in 1971 we gave in. The pretext was that there was diversion of medical cannabis to recreational use. The reality was that two GPs in London had been prescribing cannabis tincture and encouraging people to drop it onto tobacco and then smoke it. If two GPs had done something similar with morphine, it's inconceivable that this drug would have been banned but cannabis was different because the US had it in their sights. The ban of course had zero impact on recreational use, indeed, it might even have accelerated it. For in 1971 it was estimated that about half-a-million UK adults had used cannabis, then 40 years later the number was over ten million, a 20-fold increase, and probably market saturation. Despite its being illegal more people now smoke cannabis than tobacco.

The departure of Blair led to even greater attacks on cannabis users by his successor Gordon Brown, and not just because of his support for the Scottish Whisky industry. Until 2005 under English common law everyone had recourse to the defence of necessity, a centuries old, legal precedent that said, in effect, that it was possible to defend oneself against a criminal prosecution by arguing that breaking the criminal law was necessary to prevent a greater harm. For example, breaking a window might not be a crime if by doing so you were escaping from a burning building.

Evidence of the benefits of medical cannabis became more prominent in the early parts of this century and countries like The Netherlands and a number of US states then made it available. In 2000 our own House of Lords wrote an impressive review of its potential and strongly argued for a relaxation of the current regulations to allow more research, and for a year or two the government appeared to comply. It seems likely that the Blunkett review of cannabis by the ACMD was encouraged by the Lords' report. This seeming opening-up of Establishment attitudes to medical cannabis meant it was natural for patients in the UK to try it for themselves. But the government soon altered its tune and decided that there were more votes in waging a war on users, even if they were seriously disabled, and encouraged the police to prosecute.

Many of these patients had disabling and often untreatable disorders such as multiple sclerosis which made them wheelchair bound. Such disabilities didn't stop the police breaking down their doors in dawn raids to catch them 'green handed.' Many were repeatedly targeted because their whereabouts were fixed and they couldn't run away during the raid. They were sitting targets. Worse, after the third offence their liberty was completely in the hands of the local police because if they were caught for a fourth time, English law stated that then they *must* go to prison, something that a wheelchair user would find almost impossible to cope with.

For a number of years, such medical cannabis users were pleading the defence of necessity in court and getting off. Juries found that breaking the law on cannabis possession was warranted as it helped mitigate a worse evil, that of chronic pain or suffering. The Brown government was not pleased and so it asked the Law Lords to review the situation. In 2005, Lords Bingham, Carswell and Rodger decided that *for cannabis only* the defence of necessity would no longer be allowed. So one can still plead in court that the cocaine you were caught with was necessary to aid your headaches and you might get away with it, but for cannabis this is not allowed. This means everyone that is taken to either a magistrate's court or Crown Court is convicted. The illness necessitating their cannabis use may be used in mitigation of sentence, but they *must* be convicted. Magistrates hated this new law because it removed any discretion from their decision-making and only for the illegal drug that most saw as the least harmful.

Why did the Law Lords come to such a draconian decision? In their judgement they observed that 'the Court was influenced by the government's refusal to relax the legislation in this context despite recommendations to do so by the House of Lords Select Committee.' This statement suggests a degree of political pressure or influence on the decision that undermines the pretext that our judiciary is truly independent. But even more disappointing was the fact that Lord Bingham had just a couple of years earlier actively opposed criminalising cannabis users. In a dialogue with the editor of the *Spectator*, one Boris Johnson, Bingham was asked 'So you would legalise cannabis?' to which he replied, 'Absolutely. It is stupid having a law which isn't doing what it is there for.' Can there be a worse example of judicial integrity being turned by an ermine collar?

In some ways the police behaved even less honourably as they began to use the new Proceeds of Crime Act 2002 (PCA) to intimidate and persecute the partners of those convicted of cannabis possession. The PCA is a piece of legislation designed to catch and confiscate the proceeds of serious criminals who may have made millions from, e.g. importing, manufacturing or selling classified drugs. But it became misused by the police to intimidate and victimise helpers of medical cannabis patients.

Many patients with severe disability are unable to go and 'score' their own cannabis, relying on partners or friends to get it for them. These individuals would often 'own up' to doing this in an attempt to exculpate the patient from any crime. This turned out to be a big mistake for the police could then pursue them under the PCA as suppliers of cannabis. This offence carries with it a maximum of 14 years in prison (whereas the simple possession offence of the patient has a maximum of two years). But worse, by pursuing this prosecution the police were then allowed to seize their assets and passports and freeze their credit cards and bank accounts until their trial. In effect they are made functionally bankrupt with often disastrous consequences, e.g. they could no longer pay their mortgage or even buy food. Eventually, once their finances were examined and it became clear that they were not real cannabis 'dealers' the financial constraints would be lifted but this could take months or years and, in the meantime, a great deal of hurt was inflicted. I suspect most of you would agree that attacking patients using cannabis was a vindictive and unnecessary activity, and thus (just one example of) misuse of the real intentions of the PCA.

The battle against cannabis Round Three rolled on in government too. One afternoon when I happened to be in the Home Office my scientific secretary told me to come and watch an interview of Gordon Brown on TV. He made the remarkable statement that the government was going to review cannabis classification yet again because 'skunk is lethal.' We looked at each other in amazement — why was the PM talking about cannabis without consulting us? And where did this evidence of lethality come from? It turned out that we never knew for sure why Gordon Brown had said this but the best evidence we have is that he did a deal with the *Daily Mail* in preparation for the upcoming (2010) general election. Several years later, after the election, I was talking with a senior BBC figure about this episode and they told me about an 'off-the-record' meeting that Brown was alleged to have had with Paul Dacre, the then editor of the *Daily Mail*. This meeting was ostensibly a breach of protocol as un-minuted, off-the-record meetings by Prime Ministers with senior newspaper editors are against the ministerial code. But it seems to have happened and it is alleged that a 'deal' was done.

Why did Brown go to the *Daily Mail* when Blair had won his elections because of the support of the Murdoch press, especially the *Sun* and the *Times*? It was because Gordon had been quite outspoken about Murdoch's media empire and didn't want to apologise, so he tried to get some right-wing voter support from the *Daily Mail* instead. This was a strange decision as the *Daily Mail* was arguably the most right-wing paper in the UK, so an unlikely bedfellow for New Labour, even if it wasn't remotely as left-wing as Old Labour. But the *Daily Mail* had the power of a huge readership and Paul Dacre and David Cameron (the leader of the Tory party at the time) had it seems a strong mutual dislike. So, if the *Daily Mail* had supported Brown, he rather than Cameron might have won the election.

The details of the lunch are unsubstantiated but it is rumoured that Brown asked Dacre if the *Daily Mail* would support New Labour in the forthcoming election. Dacre allegedly said he would direct his newspaper to do this if Brown promised three actions. The first was to reduce the top rate of income tax to 45 per cent. The second to put a cap on immigration, and the third was to move cannabis back to Class B in the MDA 1971. Gordon agreed to all three and the 'skunk is lethal' speech was the starting gun for the build-up to another review of cannabis by the ACMD.

Brown in fact kept his side of the bargain, the top rate of tax was reduced and a cap on immigration instigated (though not achieved) and cannabis was reclassified though not without a fight. Perhaps as Brown should have predicted from its history (after all in the 1930s it had supported the Nazis), the *Daily Mail* did not honour its part of the deal and Brown lost the election.

The third ACMD cannabis review in a decade began with three main concerns being vented. In addition to the harms of skunk there were also the issues of cannabis and schizophrenia and cannabis and driving. The ACMD brought in a number of experts on each topic and reviewed the data, particularly new information since the prior reviews, in detail.

In relation to skunk we concluded that it was not lethal, though it might be somewhat more harmful, especially in terms of some brain functions, than traditional herbal or resin cannabis. Over the past decade skunk had become the most common form of cannabis sold on the streets, with police seizures showing it massively dominated the market. The reason for this rise were twofold. The first is that customs officials had made significant impacts on the smuggling of resin and herbal cannabis from traditional supply countries such as Morocco and Lebanon. UK suppliers then turned to growing their own cannabis and, in an attempt to maximise profits, used growing conditions, e.g. round the clock artificial light, that enhanced d9THC production in the plants. The second reason was that as cannabis use increased so much from the 1970s to the 2000s some users started seeking stronger variants, probably as they had developed some tolerance to the traditional strains.

Should we be worried about skunk? Skunk differs from traditional cannabis in two ways. It is stronger in terms of d9THC (the active 'stoning' ingredient) with a concentration of d9THC around three times that of traditional cannabis (so on average 15 per cent versus five per cent). Also, when the plant is forced to grow an enhanced d9THC concentration it loses the capacity to make the other main ingredient cannabidiol. This is a non-psychoactive ingredient that may have medicinal properties (see later) but which also seems to act to moderate some of the more extreme effects of d9THC. For example, it can attenuate the pro-psychosis actions and might mitigate the addiction propensity of d9THC.

A stronger concentration of d9THC per unit of plant material doesn't necessarily mean that more harm will be caused. I was asked to give evidence on this in the Dutch Parliamentary hearing on cannabis when they were considering making high strength cannabis (that with over 15 per cent d9THC content) illegal. Currently all forms cannabis in The Netherlands can be used in small amounts without fear of prosecution. I used the example of alcohol to make my case that a ban was not necessary. Alcohol comes in different concentrations; beer usually has four-to-six per cent alcohol content, wine ten-to-15 per cent and spirits 30-to-40 per cent. Drinking wine or spirits by the litre would of course cause more harms than drinking beer by the litre but except in rare cases people don't do that. We all know the relative alcohol concentrations and adjust our intake accordingly. Also, to dissuade us from excessive intake of strong alcohols the government taxes them more than the weaker ones.

The same is true for skunk in comparative terms. When experienced users are given a stronger form of cannabis to smoke they inhale less so avoid excessive intoxication. However, it is possible that naïve users will not be aware of the difference and so may accidentally get over-intoxicated early in their cannabis-using career. The Dutch approach minimises this risk because most cannabis is purchased in cannabis shops (cafés) where the content is known and advice to users can be given by the sales staff. In the UK, our blind pursuit of prohibition means that all cannabis is sourced from the black market where there is little if any quality control. The average UK user of cannabis has virtually no idea what strength of cannabis they are getting so is much more likely than their Dutch counterpart to accidentally overdose. However, the remarkable safety of cannabis — more than 1,000 times that of alcohol per intoxicating dose — means that not even skunk is lethal! It was the absurd punitive attack by the last Labour government on cannabis users that has led to the development of new synthetic cannabinoids that can be lethal, and this worrying new problem will be discussed later.

The vehicle driving issue was something we had dealt with in previous ACMD reviews. Cannabis intoxication clearly impairs driving performance but in a different manner to alcohol. Stoned people have more insight into their impairment than many drunken ones do, so they drive less and, when they do, take less risks. They are also less impulsive, as cannabis appears to enhance restraint whereas alcohol disinhibits it (compare the impact of the two drugs on violent behaviour also). The government's own experts on road accidents from drugs concluded that cannabis had only around one quarter the risk of an accident compared with alcohol and more recent data suggest that there may be no increased risk at all.

The third issue was that of schizophrenia. This is a devastating disorder that strikes mostly young people in the transition to adulthood and effectively ruins the rest of their lives. Despite nearly a century of research spanning family, adoption to biological and genetic studies we still have little idea of what causes it. In some ways finding the cause of schizophrenia is the Holy Grail of psychiatry, because we presume that once this is identified then more effective treatments, or even preventions, will be developed.

In my lifetime in medicine I have seen some of the top psychiatrists take on this challenge. They have developed and tested theories relating to influenza infection in-utero, other early developmental problems, having Caribbean ancestry and the stress of living in cities being the most prominent. But all have been refuted or at least floundered as replication studies failed. Then came the massive rise in cannabis use from the 1960s. This meant that by the new millennium many young people with schizophrenia had prior exposure to cannabis. Also, the effects of intoxication with cannabis to some extent mimics the symptoms of schizophrenia—at least the paranoia and confused thinking. The group of John Krystal at Yale University have even used d9THC in human volunteers as a model of psychosis. So, the idea developed that maybe cannabis use was causing some cases of schizophrenia. This was appealing to both psychiatrists and parents for two reasons. First, it gave them something to try to change, if you could stop people with schizophrenia from smoking cannabis maybe some would recover; if you could stop them from ever smoking it then maybe some cases of psychosis would never emerge. Second, it gave them something or someone to blame—the drug, the dealer, the patient—and this was a powerful motivation.

Parents especially wanted an explanation for their children's illness and cannabis was an easy answer. Some parents even began to criticise their schizophrenic offspring for having brought the disorder on themselves through smoking cannabis. This is an understandable reaction but one that is exceptionally unhelpful and often quite damaging to anyone with schizophrenia. Parental hostility (technically called negative expressed emotion) has for decades been known to worsen outcomes in people with this disorder.

Despite a further ten years of research it is still unclear whether cannabis causes schizophrenia. We examined the UK Medical Research Council GP database to see if the massive (20-fold) increased use of cannabis from the 1970s to the present day had been accompanied by any increase in the number of people with either pure schizophrenia or with psychosis in general and found no relationship. If anything, the number of cases of both these diagnoses fell as cannabis use increased. The same is true in all western countries where there has been similar increased use of cannabis over the past five decades. However, there is some suggestion that cannabis use might bring forward the onset of schizophrenia in people who are predisposed to getting it anyway. Also, the balance of evidence from the UK now suggests that whilst the use of traditional herbal cannabis is not associated with psychosis, the use of strong skunk may worsen symptoms of schizophrenia in people who use it a lot.

Overall, any association between cannabis and schizophrenia appears to be correlative rather than causative, or even that predisposition to schizophrenia might lead to cannabis use. Many people with schizophrenia use cannabis and, in some cases, this may exacerbate their symptoms. Why they use it when it makes some symptoms, especially auditory hallucinations (hearing voices) worse is still hotly debated and there are many possible reasons. One is that smoking cannabis gives them some reduction from other symptoms such as slowed thinking and may enhance appreciation of other activities, e.g. music. Another idea is that cannabis helps reduce the adverse effects of their medication, such as stiffness of their muscles. In some cases, cannabis can also help sleep and appetite. Cannabis can reduce anxiety, and many people with schizophrenia live in poor localities and conditions, often suffering significant stress from neighbours, which increases anxiety.

Another set of reasons for cannabis use in the schizophrenia population are social. People with schizophrenia often have little to do, few are employed, and they have boring, routine lives, so cannabis use can help pass the time. They are also easy targets for drug dealers who befriend them and then fleece them for money.

Most intriguingly there is some evidence that some chemicals found in cannabis particularly cannabidiol may actually reduce psychosis and a recent trial has confirmed this. The implications of this finding are profound for it means that the prohibitionist policy designed to reduce cannabis use and harms has had exactly the opposite effect. It led to the rise of skunk which appears to be more psychosis-provoking and addiction-forming than the traditional forms of cannabis it has replaced. The cannabis-causes-schizophrenia campaigners for cannabis prohibition have inadvertently made things worse for the users of cannabis, including many people with schizophrenia!

Of course, this is not the first time that drug laws have made things worse rather than better. We have already seen how attempts to block MDMA production via seizing safrole in 2005 led to a sudden spike in deaths from PMA. Other examples include the international ban on opium smoking in 1912 leading to the rise of heroin injecting, alcohol prohibition leading to methanol drinking, cocaine prohibition leading to crack use, and the rise of synthetic cannabinoids. History tells us that trying to stop the use of one drug is likely to lead to the use of more potent, and hence more dangerous, alternatives.

Taking all these issues into consideration, the ACMD and the additional experts, by a decisive majority decided to keep all forms of cannabis in Class C. We also made a whole series of other recommendations to increase research and knowledge. This report was presented to the government with several appendices. One of these related to public opinion, for as part of this review we decided to consult the public in the form of a MORI poll on cannabis regulations. We asked a representative group of the general public some simple questions regarding the legal status of cannabis. A key one was — 'What class do you think cannabis should be in?' The responses were clear: the largest group (41 per cent) wanted it to stay the same i.e. in Class C. Somewhat to our surprise we found a greater percentage (27 per cent) wanted it to be legal than the total who wanted it either Class B (13 per cent) or Class A (eleven per cent) (note that nine per cent had no opinion). These scores were revealing and we thought that since they were obtained using the same research methodology as political parties use to judge the public's view of their own policies they might carry some weight with the government. It was obvious that only a minority wanted cannabis re-classified upwards — over two thirds wanted the status quo (Class C) or lesser controls.

When I shared the final ACMD report with the Drugs Minister he said that the Home Office agreed with the whole content and all the recommendations — except one, keeping the status quo. When I enquired why he said, 'The public would not accept it.' Playing my master card I drew his attention to Appendix 2 where the results of the MORI poll were presented, and explained the results. The vast majority of the public wanted cannabis to stay Class C or lower (and even be legalised). He then spoke these memorable words: 'That's the wrong kind of public.' I had to laugh because I fully understood what he meant. Having worked with the Home Office for nearly ten years I knew they were always fretting about what the *Daily Mail* was saying about their policies and actions. We both knew that the 'right kind of public' was that newspaper's readership, not those contacted by MORI. This explained why Gordon Brown had tried to do a deal with the *Daily Mail*. Its vast readership had exceptional power in English politics.

Today the battles continue over cannabis. Despite as of November 2020 being legal in 15 states of the US and decriminalised in many others the Conservative UK government opposes this on the false grounds that cannabis is a dangerous drug. They have pursued policies such as urine testing of prisoners for cannabis use that has led to the rise of synthetic cannabinoids (aka spice) that are now rife in our prisons and amongst our street people. Synthetic cannabinoids were responsible for over 60 or more deaths of prisoners last year, yet cannabis never killed any prisoner.

The battle against recreational cannabis put medical cannabis on the back burner for until 2018 the government also denied the medical value of cannabis. They were forced to change tack in 2017 following high profile medical cases of children with severe epilepsy that was only responsive to medical cannabis. The families of these children were forced at great expense to live abroad in countries where medical cannabis was available, or fly to Holland each month to collect a prescription. Many were paying over £2,000 per month to treat their child, and some were forced to sell their homes to cover these costs. This huge financial burden on the parents came despite improvement in the children's symptoms, massively reducing their NHS cost burden through reduced expenditure on other medicines and fewer admissions to hospital.

The media and public outcry against legal regulations denying these children their only proven treatment led, in November 2018, the UK's chief medical officer — Professor Sally Davies — to state that there was sufficient evidence of the medical value of cannabis to have it removed from Schedule 1 of the

MDA 1971. Plant-derived medical cannabis was put into Schedule 2, alongside much more dangerous drugs such as heroin and fentanyl, but at least it could be prescribed.

Or could it? In the 20 months since this re-scheduling there have been fewer than 20 prescriptions within the NHS. Despite the UK having no restrictions on the disorders medical cannabis can be used for, it has hardly been prescribed. Not even to the children in whom it has been proved to improve their epilepsy. The reasons for this are complex. In part they reflect ignorance—in some cases wilful ignorance—on the part of many doctors who don't want to accept that their anti-cannabis views are wrong. Also, National Institute for Health and Care Excellence (NICE) guidance has been quite negative. Worse, medical cannabis was treated as being an 'off licence' medicine: it was made a 'special,' so that each prescription had to be authorised and no more than one month's supply could be prescribed at any one time. Since all UK medical cannabis is imported this meant huge pharmacy delays and vastly increased costs. Finally, the NHS seemed unwilling to pay for medical cannabis despite the likely cost savings for each patient.

In order to mitigate this cruel deceit—giving medical cannabis with one hand and taking it away with the other—the charity Drug Science, the subject of *Chapter 10*, has set up a UK-wide network of private prescribers of medical cannabis. The project is called TWENTY21 and has the vision of having 20,000 patients enrolled by the end of 2021. The initiative has been funded by unrestricted grants from six medical cannabis companies who are supplying a range of different medical cannabis products at cost price, so most patients will have to pay no more than £150 per month for their medicine. All patients are entered into a web-based database so that details of the type of cannabis use, clinical response and adverse effects can be collected on everyone enrolled. In this way we hope to get enough data on efficacy and safety so that by 2022 we can convince the medical profession and the NHS of the value of medical cannabis, so undoing the current block.

In *Chapter 10* there is more on the history, pharmacology and international politics of cannabis.

CHAPTER 8

The Scale of Harms

I mentioned in *Chapter 7* that when I had the pleasure of working on the Runciman Committee I began to develop a scale to measure the harms of drugs. Initially this was a nine-point scale with three sections, each of three questions, and each question was scored on a one-to-three point scale, with more harm attracting more points, giving a maximum score of 27 points.

- The first section estimated the *physical* harms of drugs to the person using them. One measure estimated the acute (immediate) harms of the drug (e.g. was it likely to kill you as soon as you took it). The second the harms when used repeatedly; and the third the harms from intravenous (IV) use.

- The second section covered the *dependence liability* of drugs in terms of intensity of pleasure (liking), psychological dependence (craving) and physical dependence (severity of withdrawal).

- The third section covered *harms to society*, from intoxication, other social harms (e.g. damage to families from drug habits, people from road traffic accidents) and health care costs.

Using this scale, I estimated that heroin was the most harmful drug and cannabis the least. The committee agreed and we obtained external validation from a number of addiction psychiatrists in the UK's Royal College who agreed largely with our ranking. Based on this assessment the committee recommended that the Misuse of Drugs Act 1971 be modified. We thought the three classes

A, B and C were still useful but that some drugs were in the wrong classes and so should be moved to better represent their relative harms.

The key recommendations were hardly radical. We suggested that, based on evidence of harms, cannabis should move from A and B (where different forms were) to C and that ecstasy (MDMA) and psychedelics should move down from A to B. The media agreed and at the press launch we were actively criticised by several papers for being too conservative and cautious in our advice. Even the government seemed to agree. As I have already explained, following the House of Lord's recommendation a policy of liberalisation of cannabis for medical use had been initiated, and our report gave impetus to the Blunkett review of cannabis products that eventually led to the regrading of cannabis to Class C in 2004. The other recommendations fell on deaf ears. The ACMD were refused permission to review MDMA for nearly a decade and psychedelics were severely hammered a few years later when magic mushrooms were brought into the MDA 1971 as Class A drugs! But more of that later.

The initial wide-ranging support for the Runciman report's recommendations put me into the public eye for the first time as the UK's expert on addiction and drugs. Soon after I was asked to consider joining the ACMD as the Chair of the Technical Committee, as the previous Chair, Professor Malcolm Lader, was stepping down. I went along to a meeting of the committee to explore the challenge this might entail and was disturbed by what I encountered. The committee was full of experienced and talented academics and clinicians, but the process of harm assessment was opaque and unstructured. Statements such as 'Ecstasy will never be downgraded while I am on this committee' surprised me as being more emotion than science-based. So, I agreed to chair this group provided I could instigate a systematic review of the drug classification system using a defined and transparent process. The Home Office agreed, and we got going.

At every meeting of the committee (three per year) the group assessed a number of drugs using my nine-point scale. We all did it and the scores of each person were presented to the group for discussion. This is the Delphic approach which uses group expertise to come to the best estimate of knowledge in areas where facts are uncertain or absent. People were asked to explain and, in a few cases, defend extreme positions until a consensus was reached. We also took evidence from our Dutch equivalent group who had instigated a similar process for evaluating new drugs that were emerging into the recreational market.

Over several years we covered 20 different drugs. Most were controlled under the MDA 1971 but some (alcohol, ketamine, tobacco, alkyl nitrites (poppers) and khat) were legal. The results are shown in the list below and were published in the leading medical journal *The Lancet* in 2007. Each drug was scored against a maximum of 30:

- Heroin — 27
- Cocaine — 23
- Barbiturates — 21
- Methadone — 19
- Alcohol — 18
- Ketamine — 17
- Benzodiazepines — 17
- Amphetamines — 16
- Cigarettes — 16
- Cannabis — 14
- Buprenorphine -13
- Solvents — 13
- Methylamphetamine (i.e. 4-MTA) — 14
- LSD — 14
- Anabolic steroids — 12
- GHB — 11
- MDMA — 11
- Poppers — 9
- Khat — 8.

> Source: Nutt, D J, King, L A, Saulsbury, W and Blakemore, C, Development of a rational scale to assess the harm of drugs of potential misuse. The above list was reproduced in the form of a graph in *The Lancet* (2007, 369:1047-1053 PMID: 17382831).

These findings attracted a lot of attention, not least because there is clearly little correlation between the harms of drugs and whether they are in the MDA 1971 or not. Also, the scientific integrity of the Act was questioned as there was no correlation between the class of a drug in the Act and its harms. The 1971

Act had failed in its major aims — to provide scientific, evidence-based measures of drug harms for sentencing purposes. It was clearly not fit for purpose.

Few people noted that ketamine, then still a legal drug scored in the top half, just alongside alcohol. This analysis provided the first insights into the harms of this dissociative sedative and was the prelude to the ACMD recommending it being controlled under the Act, something that occurred soon afterwards.

We were criticised widely. The anti-smoking lobby argued that as cigarettes were the leading cause of premature death in the world then tobacco should be the No. 1 most harmful drug. But this failed to appreciate the intentions of our approach. We covered *all* the harms of drugs, not just life years lost to premature death. Smoking is very harmful to users, half of all cigarette smokers die from a smoking-related illnesses. But they tend to die in their 50s or older, whereas deaths from heroin and alcohol are much more likely in younger people. Moreover, the impact of smoking on society is less than that of alcohol in terms of harms to others such as violence and road traffic accidents.

The drinks industry said we were misguided because we only looked at the harms, not the benefits of drugs, and that alcohol had health benefits (these claims we have exposed as being mostly wrong in *Chapter 5*). The anti-cannabis campaigners said it was more harmful because it was more widely used than drugs that scored above it — etc., etc.

Yet in all the criticism a voice of support came in the form of an email from Professor Larry Phillips at the London School of Economics. It simply said, 'Well done David, but you could do it much better if you used MCDA. Happy to help if interested.' I had never heard of MCDA — which I discovered stands for multi-criteria decision analysis. So, with Professor Colin Blakemore, the then head of the Medical Research Council (MRC) and a co-author of the *Lancet* paper, a meeting with Larry was arranged. Here he explained the methodology of MCDA — and the power of it. He had used it to help the UK government decide on what to do with one of the great environmental problems of our times — how best to deal with nuclear waste. Surely it could help us make sensible decisions about drugs?

To start with, the MRC and the Home Office were supportive and both organizations put up £10,000 to allow us to convene a meeting to kick start the process. The first thing we had to do was decide on what harms there were of drugs that needed to be taken into consideration. The ACMD council was invited to a weekend meeting at Cumberland lodge, a conference venue in

Windsor Great Park. About 30 of us were locked away for an intensive meeting that started with us writing down on post-it notes every harm of drugs we could imagine. These were extremely wide-ranging from health harms to drug users, through social harms to international harms — e.g. deforestation of the Amazon jungle to grow cocaine.

By the end of the first session thousands of harms were collected and collated across multiple tables in the large conference room. That was the easy part. The next session was spent finding sets of similar harms: we had to coalesce them into a series of related topics and after several hours of moving around the little patches it emerged that there were 16 clusters representing the 16 different harms of drugs. Nine of these were harms to users of drugs and seven harms to society (we called them 'harms to others'). *Table 1* below sets out the 16 different ways (parameters) in which drugs can cause harm — and the definitions of each.

Name	Description
DRUG SPECIFIC MORTALITY	Intrinsic lethality of the drug expressed as ratio of lethal dose and standard dose (for adults). 100 = an inverted ratio of 33% (ratio of 3 —> 1/3) 50= an inverted ratio of 10% (ratio of 10 —>1/10) 0 = an inverted ratio of 0%.
DRUG RELATED MORTALITY	The extent to which life is shortened by the use of this drug (excludes drug specific mortality). E.g. road traffic accidents, lung cancers, HIV, suicide.
DRUG SPECIFIC DAMAGE	Drug specific damage to physical health, e.g. cirrhosis, seizures, strokes, cardiomyopathy, stomach ulcers.
DRUG RELATED DAMAGE	Drug related damage to physical health, including consequences of e.g. sexual unwanted activities and self-harm, blood born viruses (BBV), emphysema, damage from cutting agents.
DEPENDENCE	The extent to which this drug creates a propensity or urge to continue to use despite adverse consequences (ICD10 or DSM4).
DRUG SPECIFIC IMPAIRMENT OF MENTAL FUNCTIONING	Drug specific impairment of mental functioning, e.g. amphetamine induced psychosis, intoxication.

Name	Description
DRUG-RELATED IMPAIRMENT OF MENTAL FUNCTIONING	Drug-related impairment of mental functioning. E.g. mood disorders secondary to drug-users lifestyle or drug use.
LOSS OF TANGIBLES	Extent of loss of tangible things (e.g. income, housing, job, educational achievements, criminal record, imprisonment).
LOSS OF RELATIONSHIPS	Extent of loss of relationship with family and friends.
INJURY	The extent to which the use of this drug increases the chance of injuries to others both directly and indirectly, e.g. violence (including domestic violence), traffic accidents, foetal harm, drug waste, secondary transmission of blood born viruses (BBVs).
CRIME	The extent to which the use of this drug involves or leads to an increase in the volume of acquisitive crime (beyond the use-of-drug act) directly or indirectly (at the population level, not the individual). 100 = the most 'harmful' (on a 'relative' scale) 0 = no harm.
ENVIRONMENTAL DAMAGE	The extent to which the use and production of this drug causes environmental damage locally, e.g. toxic waste from amphetamine factories, discarded needles.
FAMILY ADVERSITIES	The extent to which the use of this drug causes family adversities, e.g. family breakdown, loss of economic wellbeing, emotional well-being, future prospects of children, child neglect.
INTERNATIONAL DAMAGE	The extent to which the use of this drug in the UK contributes to damage at an international level, e.g. deforestation, destabilisation of countries, international crime and new markets.
ECONOMIC COST	The extent to which the use of this drug causes direct costs to the country (e.g. healthcare, police, prisons, social services, customs, insurance, crime) and indirect cost (e.g. loss of productivity, absenteeism).
COMMUNITY	The extent to which the use of this drug creates decline in social cohesion and decline in the reputation of the community.

We then had to develop acute and agreed definitions of each of these harms so that they could be evaluated by us, and by other groups that wanted to follow our lead. This proved challenging and took most of the next day. But by departure time on the Sunday afternoon it was all done. We had the harms and their definitions so were ready to start using them on different drugs. We agreed to organize a further two-day meeting in a few months time to complete the process. Little did we know that I wouldn't be around to organize this, since a few weeks later I was sacked! More on this is in the next chapter. But despite my being sacked, or maybe because it liberated us from the controlling influence of the Home Office, we were able to conduct the most detailed analysis of drug harms ever undertaken using the MCDA approach under the guidance of Larry Phillips.

The process is a sophisticated one. But all decisions are conducted openly and transparently in true Delphic fashion and if any member disagrees then they have to say so and argue their case in front of the others. Each of the 16 parameters of harm is rated on a zero-to-100 scale with the most harmful drug on that parameter put at 100. Then the group has to decide the relative level of harm of the other 19 drugs in relation to this one.

An example will make this easier to understand. Take the first parameter: Drug Specific Mortality. The likelihood of a drug killing you each time you use it. Clearly heroin is at the top as Les King, one of our expert chemists, had shown recently in terms of deaths per number of times used it scores way higher than any of the other drugs. Then each other drug is scaled on the zero-to-100 scale as a ratio of its harm to that of heroin. So, drugs half as likely to kill from each use would score 50, one a tenth would score 10, and one a hundredth would score 1. Drugs without impact on that harm would score 0. This process is then continued for each parameter so that eventually 16 ratio scales are completed. That's the first part over.

The second stage is to weight each of these scales against each other. This is done because it is unlikely that each parameter matters the same. But the question of which matters more is a subjective one and has to be decided by the group. In essence the difference between the top and bottom drug on each parameter is considered and the group decides which it cares about most.

For example, in our group when considering the harms to others the economic scale was given the highest score — largely because of the huge economic impact of the top drug—alcohol. This parameter was scored 100 and then the group decided how much it cared about the other four parameters. The group cared about crime quite a lot, giving it a score of 80 per cent that of economic damage, but environmental damage they cared about only 35 per cent as much.

Once all the weightings are done then the computer programme (HiLife) adjusts all the scales by the percentage weights and a final ranking is produced for the total scores on all 16 parameters. This is the now famous graph shown below. It has become a meme of advocates for drug policy reform.

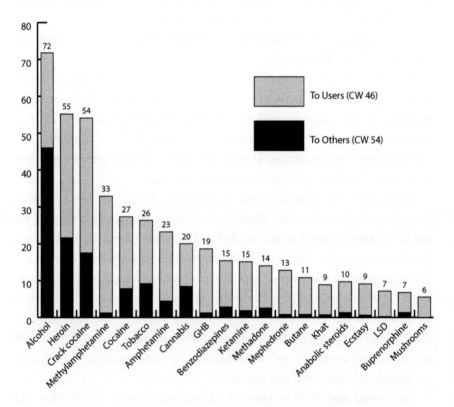

Figure 1: Drugs ranked according to total harm. Reproduced from the author's own data (2010), a version of which first appeared in *The Lancet*.

The results were surprising to me—alcohol had moved up from being just fifth most harmful in the 2007 study to the most harmful in this one. The reason is clear—the modern MCDA approach gives much more consideration to the impact of drugs on society, on other people's lives. It's obvious by the height of that bar that alcohol is by far the most harmful drug to others. We all know this; never a day goes by without some news article of alcohol damage on the roads, to our health, violence to others, etc. Alcohol is not the most harmful drug to the user, as shown in *Figure 1* above, crack cocaine is. But still alcohol is the fourth most harmful drug to the user, so in total it's the most harmful in the UK. I had long argued that reducing the harms of alcohol should be a major target for government and now I had even more proof I was right.

The paper was accepted and quickly published by the *Lancet* and got quite a lot of attention. I was interviewed about it on the Today programme where the other discussant was Peter Hitchens who said what we had done was not scientific and called me a 'ninny brain'. This caused uproar amongst BBC Radio 4 listeners many of whom complained on my behalf.

But how can we be sure we were correct? The best way was to get another independent group to replicate our study and this we were able to do by obtaining a grant from the European Department of Justice. This department of the EU has for some time been interested in using modern approaches to assist in deciding on drug policy and penalties. They funded us to repeat the analysis on the same 20 drugs but this time using the expertise of a group of 30 European experts from 20 different European countries.

So, Larry Phillips conducted another MCDA but this time in Brussels. These 30 European experts adjusted the rankings of every one of the 16 parameters of harm. They also changed all the weightings, deciding that drug-related mortality was the one they cared most about. But after the computer had done its work the results were almost indistinguishable from the UK data. Only one drug had changed place, gammahydroxybutrate (GHB) and a Spearman's correlation between the two sets of scores showed a remarkable 0.995 match. This tells us the MCDA drug harm assessment process is robust, and so meaningful in terms of directing policy.

In 2018 we assisted a group of Australian drug experts to conduct their own MCDA on the drugs of relevance to that country. Australia has a large and growing methamphetamine problem from home-made sources. It also has indigenous groups that use substances rarely met with in the UK and Europe such as sniffing petrol and drinking cava. We also were able for the first time to address the harms from the rising tide of synthetic opioids (fentanyls) and include them in relation to their recreational use. The result of this work was published in 2019 and showed yet again alcohol to be the most harmful drug. Methamphetamine moved up into second place with fentanyls and heroin close behind. Cava came out as low in harms as did inhaling or drinking petrol, though the latter did score highly on harm to user its low use prevalence made harms to others low.

To vape or not to vape?

Arguably the most innovative, or as we now say, disruptive technology in the drug harm-reduction space is vaping of nicotine. It may also be the most controversial innovation since safe injecting rooms for heroin users. The use of vaping developed in the 1990s by smokers who wanted a safer alternative. Small companies in the UK and US developed devices that allowed a liquid solution containing nicotine in the solvent propylene glycol. This solution is heated by a battery-powered coil and the vapour that contains nicotine is inhaled (hence the term vaping). Commonly used alternative terms include e-cigarettes and, in our analysis, we called them by the generic term electronic nicotine delivery systems (ENDS).

Vapers usually report that once they have decided on the best device for them, and the optimal nicotine concentration, then they are able to completely give up cigarettes. This often has a major impact on their health with a reduction in lung and chest complaints. Vaping is also far cheaper than buying cigarettes as there is no punitive excise duty taxation. From my perspective this makes vaping a major advance in tobacco harm reduction. We know that cigarette smoking leads to six million premature deaths per year and this will increase to make a total of one billion over the course of this century. So, if every smoker moved to vaping how many of these lives would be saved?

We can be fairly certain that vaping is likely to be less harmful than cigarettes because smokers change to it to improve their health. Vaping hasn't been around for long enough to have the necessary data to be completely sure but using the MCDA approach we can make the best estimate possible at the moment. This we did a few years ago when we compared the harms of a range of different nicotine products, ranging from those that burn tobacco such as cigarettes and cigars, through electronic cigarettes and snus (see further below) to pure medical nicotine products such as patches and gum.

Cigarettes turned out to be the most harmful both to the user (because they cause lung cancer, chronic lung disease, heart disease, etc.) and nicotine gum the least (it's licensed as a medicine so has to be safe). Cigarettes also turned out to be many times more harmful to others than any other form of nicotine; the reasons for this were the health harms of passive smoking and the startling fact that *half* of all the fires in the world are caused by cigarette stubs which leads to around 2,500 deaths per year and millions of hectares of land destroyed by burning.

In contrast vaping is far less harmful to both users and society. In our estimate given the data at the time, at least 25 times less harmful and maybe even less so. Apart from the fact that there are no burning stubs to cause fires other reasons for this low harm rating include the very small number of different types of toxins that vaping produces in comparison with cigarettes (where over 7,000 different ones have been found). Also, the levels of the few toxins in vaping are significantly lower than those same ones found in cigarette smoking. Together cancer and lung disease risks are reduced remarkably. There is also a benefit on cardiac health because vaping produces a much lower level of carbon-monoxide than cigarettes and it is the effect of this gas to impair oxygen transport in the blood that explains the high blood pressure and heart attack risks of cigarettes.

Our analysis also found that Swedish snus was nearly as safe as vaping. Snus is an orally administered powdered pure tobacco supplied in a pouch. It has become popular in Sweden and more recently been made available in neighbouring Norway. Because there is no burning of tobacco it doesn't produce toxins and the use of snus in Sweden has reduced the level of lung cancer deaths in that country to the lowest in Europe: Swedish men using snus have no increased risk of lung or other cigarette-related cancers.

Our data was welcomed as a major contribution to getting an informed debate on the value and risks of vaping. It was supported by a variety of experts in the field and quite soon after was used by Public Health England (PHE) to give a clear recommendation to the UK government that vaping should be endorsed and even encouraged. The Welsh government went even further and made e-cigarettes available on the NHS for people with chronic smoking-related bronchitis to reduce lung inflammation and so reduce hospital admissions.

But not everyone working in the field of tobacco harm reduction was happy with our findings. Those whose ambition was to eliminate all cigarette smoking were upset because up to that point they had been vilifying vaping as being as harmful as smoking cigarettes. Now we had exposed the fallacy in that argument, they flew into a rage and started to try to undermine our findings — but they couldn't deny the evidence. So in the time-honoured tradition of those who didn't like the message, they attacked the messengers, in this case Drug Science and PHE. We were accused of being in the pockets of the tobacco industry, and even that British American Tobacco had written the report for us! There were several potentially libelous editorials in the *Lancet* and *British Medical Journal* (BMJ) suggesting we were being influenced by the industry, to which we replied forcibly.

Eventually our arguments were accepted by the *Lancet* but the BMJ refused to apologise which led to some fascinating interchanges. I pointed out that the editorials were wrong and showed them an email trail that we believed showed bias against us. This we felt made their analysis and conclusions unsafe and indeed incorrect. But this they resisted.

So, I approached the Committee on Publication Ethics (COPE) for guidance. As the editor of the *Journal of Psychopharmacology* I was a member of this association and had helped them with questionnaires in the past. The question I posed was simple — was it ethical for a journal to continue to allow in its archive an editorial that they had been told (and that we believed) was wrong?

After many months and several prompts, I got their reply. They said the role of COPE was not to adjudicate on specific issues or questions relating to real conflict over ethics, it just gave guidance to editors as to how to handle these issues themselves! Truly a cop-out. But I wasn't going to give up that easily so I replied asking what advice they would give to an editor like me how to handle such a question if it were to emerge in the future? Years later and as yet they have not replied. Their cop-out might well be true, but it wasn't a justification for not apologising to us for what seemed to be an *insulting* and professionally libellous editorial.

The attacks on our analysis still didn't go away and in fact came to a head with an article in the *Times* in 2016. A *Times* reporter at a conference was told by one of our opponents that we had been paid by the tobacco industry to find evidence to support vaping. They stated this in an article in their newspaper on vaping. This assertion was we felt clearly libellous so we hired a senior QC who agreed, and we threatened that we would sue the *Times* unless they retracted and apologised. Retract they did but held out against a formal published apology. We persisted and won and the actual apology that was printed in the paper is shown below. It was a remarkable win for Drug Science and the value of vaping in tobacco harm reduction.

Apology published 4 November 2016

'We recently published articles and a leader about scientists and public health experts and their alleged financial links with the tobacco industry (Tobacco giants fund vaping studies, Scientists wooed in charm offensive and Smoke in their eyes, October 12). The experts mentioned in our report, Professor David Nutt of Imperial College London, Professor David Sweanor of the Faculty of Law and Centre for Health Law, Policy & Ethics at the University of Ottawa, Professor Karl Fagerstrom who created the Fagerstrom Test for Cigarette Dependency, Professor Riccardo Polosa, Director of the Institute for Internal Medicine and Clinical Immunology at the University of Catania, and Clive Bates, former executive director of Action on Smoking and Health, are internationally respected for their longstanding global work to reduce smoking, and their work on the issue of nicotine harm reduction. Our report and a panel headed 'Academics making a packet' implied that these experts had received funding for research into e-cigarettes. We accept that this was wrong and that their work has not been tainted by the influence of tobacco industry funding. We apologise for our errors and omissions and for the embarrassment caused.'

Now, in the UK, the argument has been won — vaping is by general agreement less harmful than smoking cigarettes and is likely to be a major health improvement approach. My own view is that vaping could be the biggest health innovation since vaccination. If the billion cigarette smokers who will die from their addiction this century were to switch to vaping then how many would not die? My estimate is that perhaps most would live, maybe there would be just a few million premature deaths. So vaping could save nearly a billion lives. Nothing in health except perhaps clean water, reduced air pollution and vaccinations could come close to this kind of impact. So why would anyone oppose it? The reason is political not scientific.

Unlike the enthusiastic uptake of vaping in the UK, in the rest of the world vaping has had a much rockier ride with regulators. In the US vaping is allowed but grudgingly and with major limitations. In many countries it is banned even though cigarettes are legal and indeed advertised. In India a seller of e-cigarettes was imprisoned because they are illegal though cigarettes and chewing tobacco (which we estimated to be about twice as harmful as vaping) is actively marketed. Similarly, in China vaping is illegal, though this is perhaps more easily understood than the Indian governmental approach as the Chinese government has a monopoly on cigarette production and sales so can choose to eliminate any competition.

The biggest problem is that the World Health Organization (WHO) has opposed vaping — or at least not endorsed it. A cynic might say that this may be because the Chinese government sits on the WHO governing council so wants to protect its cigarette monopoly. Another factor is that the US government doesn't support vaping either and this has led to a major ongoing battle in the US between vaping harm reductionists and government agencies such as the Federal Drugs Administration (FDA) and National Institutes of Health (NIH) as well as campaigning groups like the Campaign for Tobacco Free Kids. Simply put, the battle is between the vaping advocates who support harm reduction and the absolute prohibitionists who wish to eliminate all forms of smoking — even ones such as vaping that are much less harmful than cigarette use, or maybe even harmless — on principle. To some extent they have succeeded as already in certain states some vaping flavours have been made illegal, supposedly to deter users.

Underpinning these arguments is the fear by many old anti-tobacco campaigners that vaping is just a new ploy by the tobacco industry to get people addicted to nicotine and so then onto cigarette use. They persevere in this paranoid position despite year-on-year evidence that vaping does exactly the opposite — it actually decreases cigarette use. This is probably because rebellious and oppositional kids who might have in the past tended to use cigarettes to anger parents and educationalists now vape. Almost no-one moves from vaping to cigarettes because the latter are so unpleasant and difficult to use in comparison with vaping. Of course, if vaping were to be banned then those vapers who are dependent on nicotine would almost certainly migrate to cigarettes. This is why keeping vaping open and available as a safer alternative is vital in the US.

This battle has seen the prohibitionists use some of the worst science ever conducted to attack vaping. Many poorly conducted papers claiming harms from vaping have been published and celebrated by the prohibitionists as proof that vaping should be banned. Most of these do not attempt to use cigarette smoking as a positive control and many use vaping procedures with temperature and current levels well outside the range used by vapers. Perhaps the most remarkable was one claiming that e-cigarette vapours when bubbled through a suspension of lung epithelium cells for many days caused cancerous-like changes. When questioned about the impact of cigarette smoke as a positive comparator that was missing the authors replied 'innocently' that this experiment wasn't possible as all the cells died in a just few hours!

This obsession with possible negative long-term effects of vaping and the disregard of the known toxicity of cigarette smoke is typical. I believe this reflects the history of tobacco control in the US. The battle by many anti-tobacco advocates against the tobacco industry was a long and bitter one that they eventually lost. Cigarettes in the US are still legal and the tobacco industry, in return for its having paid massive compensations to the states and the public, is now exempt from further legal assaults. So, the activists need a new target for their efforts (and cynics might say to keep them in employment). Thus they have turned against vaping as the new enemy. They claim that nicotine and vaping flavours, though patently less acutely toxic than cigarette smoke, *might* be harmful in the long-term. This then allows them to raise the precautionary principle — better not to use till we know they are safe. 'Remember,' they say, 'it took decades to reveal the harms of cigarettes.' But this is a naïve and illogical argument because denying access to vaping while waiting for this evidence is not only logically impossible (without people vaping for years the harms of vaping can never be assessed) but also cruel. Millions more people will die from cigarettes as a result of denying access to vaping. Maybe in the absolutist mind of the prohibitionist one death from vaping is worse than hundreds from cigarettes?

So fearful of vaping are they that they pushed to ban all vaping liquids even those that contain no nicotine and so are unlikely to be addictive. There is an argument that vaping nicotine will lead to dependence in a significant proportion of users. Many, especially young, people are aware of this and wish to avoid it and so vape liquids that just contain flavours such as menthol or cinnamon, even bubble-gum or cream cup-cake! Now, in order to restrict vaping, the anti-vaping campaigners have forced the FDA into the absurd position where they have defined *all* vaping products as tobacco, even those that contain no nicotine at all, just flavours. This gives them absolute power to ban them under current US tobacco control legislation. We really are in a science free fantasy world like the one run by the Red Queen in Alice in Wonderland who said, 'The truth is what I make it. I could set this world on fire and call it rain.' Sad days.

CHAPTER 9

The Sacking

Before I get into my sacking, I need to give some background on the way successive governments worked with the Advisory Council on the Misuse of Drugs (ACMD). Perhaps surprisingly the high point of their relationship came in the 1980s when Margaret Thatcher was in power. AIDS had been destroying lives in the US and was beginning to show up in IV drugs users (mostly heroin addicts) in the UK. It was known that the virus was being spread by shared needles so policies such as needle exchanges were the obvious way forward. The ACMD had a meeting with Mrs Thatcher to explain the situation and suggest a solution to her, but she wasn't interested. She said she wouldn't backtrack on the Tory policy of *punishing* drug users rather than *treating* them.

Reputedly, the ACMD lead then asked if she would like to be remembered as the Prime Minster who oversaw the AIDS epidemic in the UK? This severe challenge made Mrs Thatcher think carefully. After reflection she responded that if the experts thought needle exchange was the right thing then she would trust them. The policy was introduced. We don't know her reason for changing her mind; perhaps as a scientist (she was once a research chemist) in her heart she knew that evidence should trump politics? Whatever her reason, from then on the UK had control over its AIDS problem in IV drug users and this resulted in us having one of the lowest levels of HIV infection in drug users in the world. We became a model country, an exemplar of good practice harm reduction, that other countries would visit to learn optimal policies and approaches.

ACMD interchanges with later Prime Ministers were less effective. We have already heard how Tony Blair sided with the drinks industry against UK science to prevent more rational, health-friendly alcohol policies. Blair initiated and Gordon Brown progressed the New Labour policy of being hard on cannabis to appease the right-wing press and prove to the Tories that they were tougher on drugs than them. This showing off by New Labour of it's toughness over drugs reached a bizarre peak in relation to magic mushrooms. These were legal in the UK until 2005, being used by up to a million young people every year during the autumn growing season. There were few examples of serious harms and lots of people had pleasurable visual trips, sometimes with significant emotional and existential insights.

The problem came when a couple of head shops in London began to sell freeze-dried magic mushrooms. The presence of legal hallucinogens on the streets of London drove some newspapers, particularly the *Daily Mail*, into paroxysms of moral outrage. There were exaggerated stories of people going mad on this new sort of mushroom and demands that the government clamp down on their sale. The Tory party, in opposition and by then led by David Cameron, saw a political opportunity here. They started to bait New Labour as being soft on drugs and called for magic mushrooms to be banned. Blair rose to their bait and (allegedly) rather than ask the ACMD to review the question of harms — as he was required by statute to do — he pulled together his own special committee to discuss what to do. We don't know who was on this unofficial committee but believe it was police officers and legislators; certainly, it didn't have any drug experts as members.

The ACMD heard that something was being plotted in relation to magic mushrooms and so we wrote to the Prime Minister to remind him that under the MDA 1971 decisions on drug control had to be assessed by the ACMD. Things went quiet for a few weeks and we thought common sense had prevailed but then, one Tuesday, we received a letter from the Cabinet Office informing us that there would be a debate in the House of Commons about magic mushrooms in just a few days' time. We were asked for our comments on their harmfulness to which we replied that it was impossible for the ACMD to do a full review of a drug preparation such as mushrooms in just a couple of days and asked them to defer the debate till we could do a proper assessment. Our pleas fell on deaf ears and by the end of that week magic mushrooms were illegal. This was bad enough but worse was that they were put into Class A of the MDA 1971 amongst the most harmful of drugs. It was a laughable decision, magic mushrooms being treated as equivalent in harms to drugs such as crack cocaine, heroin and crystal meth. Evidence was nowhere in sight, logic had gone out of the window, all to appease the hysteria of the press.

It was at that point I realised we had a serious problem with logic and honesty in our political process. A government that could pretend that magic mushrooms were as dangerous as crack cocaine couldn't we felt be trusted on other matters. I began to wonder if we would ever put evidence in the centre of decision-making and vowed that wherever possible I would ensure that the truth about drugs was told. To this end we initiated the first public hearings of the ACMD — both for the regular business meetings and also our special assessments to review MDMA and cannabis described already. But putting the truth into the public domain was to have momentous consequences.

My dismissal

In 2009 I was asked by the Centre for Crime and Justice Studies (CCJS) at King's College London to give their annual Eve Saville Memorial Lecture. This is a prestigious lecture on topics relating to crime and punishment policies. I chose for my title, 'Estimating Drug Harms: A Risky Business?' This was a deliberate pun being in part directed at the problems I'd had with Home Secretary Jacqui Smith over the reclassification of ecstasy (see *Chapter 6*). The talk was held at King's College's Strand campus with a hundred or so attendees, including some press. It went well with plenty of pertinent questions. My Home Office ACMD team were pleased that I had made some important critical points about current policy failings in a sensible and constructive fashion.

It was only months later when a paper based on my talk was published that my problems started. This paper, in essence just a summary of many of my previous talks and publications, received significant media attention, much more than anything I had attracted before. The reason, I now with hindsight understand, was because I was at that time the Chair of the ACMD and so the leading drugs advisor to the government (I was often labelled the 'Drugs Czar' by the media). If anyone could influence government policy it was me. And I was critical of many aspects of current policies, e.g. on irrational, non-scientific classifications of drugs, the lack of investment in harm reduction programmes, etc.

Because of the press release sent out by the CCJS, the day the talk/paper was published I found myself on the BBC morning news programme being asked what was wrong with the current ABC drug classification system? I replied it wasn't evidence-based and that the Home Office's own work published in the *Lancet* in 2007 had shown that alcohol was overall more harmful than cannabis, ecstasy or LSD. I think it was the mention of a psychedelic drug that drove the subsequent media storm. Immediately after this first interview, I was on BBC local news, the BBC World Service, and many other radio stations. Not since psychedelics were banned in 1967 had anyone in a position of authority dared to speak the truth: that they were less harmful than had been made out. All these interviews were done through the local BBC studios in Bristol but shared around the UK and the globe.

A campaign to get me sacked was started by the ultra-puritan self-appointed Europe Against Drugs Group who incited the *Daily Mail* and *Daily Telegraph* to attack me as a dangerous revolutionary whose vision would destroy the moral fibre and health of the country's youth. Within hours I was being called to a meeting the next morning in London with the Home Office chief scientist and my ACMD scientific secretariat so I dutifully caught the train up to London that evening and stayed in a hotel near to the Home Office in Westminster. I was also phoned by the government chief scientist, John Beddington, who was concerned if I was OK because he was off to a meeting in Kazakhstan that weekend and so would be out of contact.

The next (Friday) morning I had breakfast with the Home Office chief scientist who asked me how I thought things had gone the day before. I replied that it was the usual storm in a teacup that occurs whenever anyone attempts to have an honest and truthful discussion about drugs, including alcohol and tobacco. We chatted about the absurdity of this and parted amicably enough. But as I left the meeting, I said to my ACMD scientific secretary that I would see him the next Monday for a talk I was doing on ketamine for BBC Radio 1. He said that perhaps we should cancel it given the storm of yesterday which was still reverberating in the newspapers that morning. I happily agreed — it would save me another trip to London and let me get on with more research back at Bristol University. As it was a pleasant morning I strolled across St James Park to get a bus to the Imperial College London campus at South Kensington where I was to take part in an MRC symposium on addiction research that I had helped organize. We were planning a strategy for the next five years of addiction research in the UK and I was speaking on our research findings in the afternoon.

Just before lunch I got an email from the BBC. It explained that, when they had enquired with the Home Office press team why the Radio 1 ketamine talk had been cancelled, they were told that my position as Chair of the ACMD was under review and asked if I wanted to comment on this. I replied that this was the first I had heard of it, so I rang my secretariat at the ACMD and asked what was going on. They said they hadn't heard anything, but would check it out with the policy team. About two hours later they got back to me and asked if I could open an email from the Home Secretary, Alan Johnson. I did and learnt that he was asking for my resignation. I replied that I wasn't going to resign because I had been telling the truth about comparative drug harms, a truth that needed to be openly discussed as it had implications for policing and punishments. Thirty minutes later a further email from my secretariat arrived explaining that I had been sacked.

Although I was due to give my presentation in just a few minutes' time I was so outraged that I composed an email to my media contacts, especially Fiona Fox at the Science Media Centre, the BBC, Sky and ITV. By the time my talk was over I had had replies from several of them and so began my fight-back. By the time the symposium was over at 5 pm that afternoon I had three film crews waiting in the main square at Imperial College for live interviews, and BBC Newsnight planned for later that evening. For the next 24 hours I maintained a barrage of press and media commentary without a single statement being issued from the government. It wasn't until the Sunday morning that Alan Johnson was allowed to appear in the media, and then he made 'a right hash' of his Sky interview, losing his temper when accused of shooting the messenger rather than responding to the message.

In Parliament the next day, when questioned by the Liberal Democrats, Johnson justified my sacking on the grounds that I had got it wrong on the harms of cannabis. He claimed my argument that cannabis didn't cause schizophrenia was wrong because when he visited Pentonville Prison 'the other day' the prison governor had told him categorically that it did! So, the evidence of three expert cannabis reviews over nine years was overruled by the opinion of a prison governor. Such is the quality of political integrity and reasoning about drugs. I subsequently learned that the government's 36 hour silence after my sacking was due to the fact that both the Science Minister and the government's chief scientist were away, one in Japan and one in Kazakhstan, so couldn't easily be contacted. Also, Gordon Brown was such a controlling PM that the Home Secretary wasn't allowed to act of his own accord. Subsequently both the Science Minister and chief scientist expressed regret and disappointment over my sacking though Alan Johnson continues to argue it was justified because 'I had been given a yellow card by Jacqui Smith so this second infringement meant I had to be sent off' — and because 'I was a legaliser.'

The impact of my sacking was felt across the UK science community. A petition to the Prime Minister to have me reinstated was set up by academic colleagues and attracted over 3,000 signatories. About half of the other scientists on the ACMD resigned in protest. Some stayed on and tried to reason with the Home Office, but when they discovered for themselves the intransigence and misplaced approach of that establishment towards drugs, a further three resigned, effectively demolishing it as a scientific organization.

One of my few friends in Parliament was Evan Harris, the Liberal Democrat member for Abingdon, who arranged for me to speak in the Houses of Parliament one lunchtime the next week. About 20 members turned up and several spoke vehemently in my favour; in fact, one of the few scientifically trained Labour members resigned the whip because Labour had shown such anti-scientific behaviour towards me. In the next weeks the Science and Technology Committee, that had to some extent provoked my being in conflict with the Home Office over their request for a review of ecstasy, had a hearing on the relationship between government and experts. This concluded that I had been badly let down by the system. It was agreed that the Home Secretary had breached the ministerial code in sacking me and Fiona Fox, the CEO of the Science Media Centre was appointed to do a review of how scientific expertise and scientists were to be treated in future. Her report was largely accepted, and this resulted in improved transparency of how the government deals with experts on their scientific committees and protects committee members from dismissal just because the government doesn't like their opinions. Now only the chairs of committees are 'sackable' by Ministers if they don't agree with them.

Outside of Parliament the media were less supportive. I became 'fair game' for the right-wing tabloids and was appalled to discover within a week of my sacking that the *Sun* was running so-called exposés on three of my four children's alleged alcohol consumption and drug-taking. They had hacked into their Facebook accounts and deliberately misinterpreted images and comments to imply they were illegally 'high.' I complained to the Press Complaints Commission who tried to block the *Sun's* publication without success. That meant the *Sun* persisted with a two-page spread in the Saturday edition with pictures of three of my four children in supposedly compromising poses.

At one level the allegations were obviously dishonest. A picture of one son holding a rolled-up cigarette was claimed to be evidence of cannabis use (a claim that the same issue of the paper also made against actor and Harry Potter star Daniel Radcliffe). The other son was shown naked in the snow outside a sauna in Sweden where he lives and where this behaviour is perfectly normal. One daughter who didn't drink had a photo of her and a friend when 16 pretending to drink when under-age, and this was taken by the *Sun* as evidence of them drinking illegally. Once these pictures were out they became 'fair game' for other newspapers and the lies were repeated the next day by the *Mail on Sunday*, the *News of the World* and then on the following Monday by the *Daily Mail*.

We continued to press the Press Complaints Commission to get the web-sites taken down and eventually, after a few weeks, the Murdoch press ones were removed, but the *Mail* ones persisted. In frustration I rang the CEO of the Press Complaints Commission and asked why he hadn't been able to remove these and his reply was chilling 'David,' he said, 'I can't do this because my boss, the Chair of the Press Complaints Commission, is Paul Dacre, the editor of the *Daily Mail*.' If ever there was an example of conflict of interest this was it!

The idea of the press regulating their own misbehaviour was clearly ridiculous and so I joined the Hacked Off campaign to get things changed. As part of this process I wrote to the Leveson Inquiry with an account of my family's abuse by the press and offered to give oral evidence. In fact. I wasn't called but my complaint was registered in the huge list of abuses of process sent to Lord Justice Brian Leveson. I suspect it was also noted by the *Daily Mail*, for the week before Paul Dacre was to give evidence to the inquiry, I discovered that the offending postings had, at last, been deleted from their website.

I am often asked if, with hindsight, I would have done anything differently to have avoided being sacked. It's a difficult question for the process of fighting my corner after being sacked was enormously demanding and stressful. There were almost daily press interactions and a constant mass of email traffic that significantly cut into my clinical and research activities and my sleep times. But the support I received from the public, e.g. nearly 20,000 supporters on Facebook and Twitter in just a few months made me realise that I was not alone. And that the case for changing the drug laws was still vital.

Another great source of support came from an unknown benefactor. Within 24 hours of the sacking I was visiting my mother in hospital where she was being treated for a broken leg when I got an email from Toby Jackson. He said he was outraged by my sacking and wanted to donate to me a significant sum of money to allow me to set up an independent version of the ACMD. 'Of course,' I replied instantly and we agreed to meet the next week when he was in London and from this the Independent Scientific Committee on Drugs (now called Drug Science) was born — but more of this in the next chapter.

CHAPTER 10

The Rise of Drug Science

The events before and after my sacking described in the previous chapter had an electrifying effect on the rest of the ACMD. Within a month the majority of the scientists on the council had resigned in support of me and the government was under fire from most intelligent parts of the media. To try to stem this criticism the remaining members were called to a meeting with the Home Secretary, Alan Johnson and his most senior Home Office civil servants. There an attempt was made to convince the others to stay, but apparently the tone was school-masterish, with them being talked down to and told what to do — even how to think — by officials. This had the opposite effect to what the Home Office had anticipated with several other members of the ACMD walking out there and then in protest, and going straight to the press to share their support for my case.

The ACMD was fatally wounded and in truth I believe that it has never really recovered its former role and status. But a major reason for that is because of the Independent Scientific Committee on Drugs — or ISCD (now called Drug Science) — that we established with the support of Toby Jackson's donation. He was appalled by the way I had been treated and gave us sufficient funds to set up and run for three years an alternative to the ACMD. This new committee would assume the role of an honest, impartial and evidence-based expert group free from any political influence. It would provide the public, media and — if they were inclined to listen — politicians with impartial facts and evidence-based analyses on drugs and drug policy.

Setting up a charity is not easy and I was fortunate that the Centre for Crime and Justice Studies (CCJS) was prepared to accept the donation and allow us to use their facilities as office space to get going. I invited all those scientists who had resigned from the ACMD to join the new group and almost all agreed.

Also, a number of eminent senior UK experts in pharmacology and neuroscience wrote in support and I asked them to join too. Within weeks we had a powerful expert group that matched the best the ACMD had ever achieved and which was of course much stronger than the residual ACMD committee as most of its scientists had resigned. An experienced social researcher and activist, Sophie Macken, at the time working for the CCJS, came on board as our first chief executive.

At the first meeting we considered several names but we settled on the Independent Scientific Committee on Drugs (ISCD). But after a couple of years we realised that this sounded too old-fashioned and governmental, so we changed to Drug Science which it has been ever since. For simplicity, in the rest of this chapter I shall refer to the committee as Drug Science.

The remit of the new charity was to 'tell the truth about drugs' and we started doing this at once. First, we set up a web-site — which was done for free by a couple of our supporters. I developed a Twitter and Facebook presence to allow us to quickly communicate our activities, and then we started to generate new evidence. The first major endeavour was to use the 16 point scale of drug harms I had developed when at the Home Office to assess the harms of different drugs using the multi-criteria decision analysis (MCDA) tool. You will have already read about the results of this in *Chapter 8,* but this type of analysis has become internationally known. The graph reproduced in that chapter has been presented all over the world and the *Lancet* paper is now my most referenced publication, with over 1,400 citations. This means that over 1,400 subsequent publications have quoted it, usually in support of their own writings. Pleasingly almost all of these have agreed with its conclusions and many have used it as the foundation to push for policy reform in different countries.

We have since continued with a range of MCDA analyses and these have become a signature output of Drug Science. One remarkable feature of this work is that most of the studies we have conducted have been published in peer-reviewed journals, sometimes the top ones. This is an aspect of our work of which we are especially proud. Peer-review means that the research is assessed by external independent experts so has to pass a stringent test of quality before being accepted as worth publishing. There can be few, if any, charities that can match this level of scientific output. We feel this is important as it means that our results cannot be diminished by the media or politicians as just the opinions of a group of academics with similar views.

Drug Science has always understood the need to have a range of expertise on our scientific committee. Currently this ranges from analytical chemistry and forensic science through to the law. It's a remarkable group and there is rarely a question from the media that one of us cannot answer. And we get a lot of those: Drug Science has become the go to source for information on drugs and drug policy for everyone from journalists to schoolchildren and their parents. Of course, keeping this all up-to--date is a challenge especially as drugs and drug policy change so frequently. Luckily, we have obtained grants from organizations such as the Open Society Foundations that allow us to keep going.

Recently we also created a new category of supporters — the Drug Science Community — members of which make regular monthly donations to help fund us. In return these supporters get preferential access to my talks and other Drug Science events as well as signed copies of this book!

Another idea to raise funds was to set up a journal. Many charities have used this approach to provide an underpinning source of revenue. We thought about a name that best summed-up the mission of Drug Science and came up with *Drug Science, Policy and Law*. A broad title that covers the wide range of interests of our charity and allows papers that may not fit easily with other more specialist publications. We were pleased to get support for this new journal from a range of international experts who formed a powerful editorial advisory board and also from the publishers Sage who agreed to host it. More important was the fact that Sage agreed to cover the costs for the first five years until we got going. Also, importantly, they agreed to make it open access. This means that the papers are freely available to anyone with an internet connection. The result of this is that we have many readers from all over the globe and the journal has gone from strength to strength. Some of its papers, like the 15 year retrospective of the change in the Portuguese drug laws, to decriminalise personal possession, have been heavily referred to and are landmarks in this field (https://drugscience.org.uk/portugal/).

How Drug Science works

The charity has two arms — one scientific and one administrative. We also have a board of trustees that provides oversight and guidance. I chair the scientific arm and David Badcock is the CEO who looks after the running of the charity. The scientific committee overseas the web-site content and research outputs. These are led by Dr Anne Schlag, an expert in policy research from King's College London. The scientific committee meets three-to-four times a year to discuss developments in drugs science and policy and to hear relevant research discoveries in our field from both our internal members and external expert speakers. We also host research meetings such as the MCDA studies mentioned above and already detailed in *Chapter 8.*

The cannabis challenge

Perhaps our most significant output is one that didn't get into a peer-reviewed journal. But it did change the whole direction of travel of the World Health Organization (WHO) in relation to medical cannabis. Cannabis is arguably the world's oldest medicine with evidence of its use from 3,000-year-old tombs in Egypt and Siberia. It has had a place in Indian and Chinese medical writings for nearly as long. Entry into the UK was not until the late-1600s when it was brought back by traders from the east, but by the 1800s it was widely used as an over-the-counter medicine being sold as an alcoholic tincture for problems such as tetanus and seizures. Its efficacy more broadly became apparent and the definitive overview was published in the *Lancet* in 1890 by Dr John Russell Reynolds. As he was Queen Victoria's physician it is believed that she used cannabis medicines, particularly for period and childbirth pains.

The demise of cannabis as a medicine and the push to eliminate recreational use began rather surprisingly when in 1933 the US Senate voted to rescind the laws on alcohol prohibition. This left the threat that the 35,000 strong army of alcohol prohibition enforcement officers (now known as the Drug Enforcement Administration or DEA) would be made redundant along with their director Harry Anslinger. To justify their continued employment, Anslinger created a new drug scare to replace alcohol — cannabis. He renamed it by its Mexican name 'marijuana' to more closely associate its use with illegal Mexican immigrants. Then working with the less scrupulous media and anti-immigrant press he created a series of fantastic scare stories about the damaging impact of cannabis. Common themes included how cannabis use would destroy American lives and lead to the rape of white women by drug-crazed immigrants, etc. Though fanciful and dishonest these scare stories served their purpose: they created enough of a moral panic amongst the public to allow the politicians to get away with banning it.

The move to make cannabis the latest Public Enemy No. 1 after alcohol worked beautifully and Anslinger's job and private army were saved. To further vilify cannabis and to remove any need for cultivation for medical use, medical cannabis was removed from the US pharmacopeia in 1934 and the rest of the world was encouraged to support the ban under the League of Nations Health Committee that had, in their 1934 report, agreed with the US that cannabis medicines had no value.

At first the UK held out against this outrageous denial of evidence of the value of medical cannabis, just as it did when there was a similar attempt by the US to eliminate heroin as a medical treatment. So, in the UK, cannabis continued as a medicine until the Misuse of Drugs Act (MDA) 1971 was brought in, that relegated cannabis to Schedule 1 (for harmful drugs with no unique medical value) as described in earlier chapters. The driver for this ban was continued pressure from the US who still cherished the illusion that, by disallowing medicinal use, recreational use could be restricted. The instigation of the MDA in 1971 gave the UK government a chance to ban cannabis medicines. The pretext was misuse by two GPs in Ladbroke Grove, London who were prescribing tincture of cannabis to patients and suggesting that it be dripped onto tobacco and smoked. Rather than just strike the GPs off the medical register the government decided to accede to the decades of US pressure and ban cannabis medicines.

The 1934 League of Nations report that cannabis had no medicinal value was relied upon to control cannabis under the 1961 UN Convention on Narcotics. Even more amazingly it persisted as the international medical guidance on cannabis until 2018, being used as justification by the WHO for keeping cannabis as a Schedule 1 controlled drug until then. Even more absurdly the 1934 report has been lost so we can't explore its evidential base and reasoning! (https://drugsci-ence.org.uk/better-late-than-never-after-82-years-the-who-reviews-cannabis/).

To try to remedy this absurd situation Drug Science approached the WHO expert committee on drug dependence in 2016 and asked if they would review medical cannabis. They told us that to do this their rules required that their committee be presented with a pre-review of the pharmacology medical evi-dence, etc. Then if they felt there was adequate data a full review could take place. The WHO explained that the reason they had continued to rely on the 1934 report was that they didn't have the resources to pay for a pre-review. This seemed odd given that each year they were producing reviews on a range of much less widely used drugs, but Drug Science took them at their word and we conducted a pre-review for them, with funding from the Open Society Foundations. This was done in strict compliance with the WHO rules for pre-reviews so they couldn't find fault with the process or contents.

Then in December 2016 together with three other authors of the review (Val Curran of Drug Science, Willem Scholten from The Netherlands and Phil Wiffen from Newcastle University) I went Geneva to present our paper at the public open session. We argued that after 84 years it was time for a review of cannabis and gave them our paper to allow this. But the WHO officers refused to accept it—saying that they could only take reviews they had commissioned. We then appealed to the expert committee members (who are external scientists and medics) to add it to their agenda as an item under any other business. The WHO lawyer refused to allow them, saying (as it turned out incorrectly) that the committee couldn't add agenda items itself.

We were, to say the least, unhappy with this outcome so we published the report on our webpage (https://drugscience.org.uk/cannabis-review-for-the-attention-of-the-who/) and made it public. It must have had an effect as the next year the WHO put out a call for a whole series of reviews on medical cannabis—covering botanics, toxicology, pharmacology, medical evidence and epidemiology. We bid to do every one for free yet, perhaps unsurpris-ingly, were not awarded a single one! Still enough other experts were given the chance to write reviews and in December 2018 the expert committee held its first ever cannabis review. As yet their decisions have not been made public, but we believe that they agreed cannabis can have medicinal value and so should be rescheduled. These recommendations are still awaiting ratification by the

UN. We suspect this long delay is because they found in favour of cannabis being a medicine, but this overturning of decades of dishonesty concerning the drug is causing the top officials and key WHO-supporting governments such as the US and China significant embarrassment, so they are looking for ways to block the decision.

Although most of the world fell into line with the 1961 UN Convention banning medical cannabis, Holland was the notable exception. They decided to allow medical and recreational use despite pressure not to do so from the US. Subsequently, a number of US states have voted to allow medical cannabis, and the total is now 34 with eleven allowing recreational use too. This meant that by 2019 over 200 million US citizens had access to medical cannabis — but not a single Brit! In 2017, the German health authorities allowed medical cannabis to be prescribed for 57 different indications and insisted that health insurers reimburse these scripts. Still the international scene continues to progress and more and more countries are working towards making cannabis a medicine and as of June 2019 over 20 countries had made medical cannabis legal.

The UK government resisted any softening of approach until the case of Billy Caldwell came to public knowledge. Billy has a rare form of childhood epilepsy called Dravet syndrome. This resulted in his having thousands of seizures a month that were not responsive to conventional anti-convulsant drugs, and these medicines also had significant adverse effects on his cognitive state. His mother tried to get medical cannabis in the UK but was denied it so she took him to the US and Canada to seek treatment. This was remarkably successful. On cannabidiol (CBD) his seizures reduced by 90 per cent and when some cannabis oil was added they disappeared completely (probably because cannabis oil contains a low concentration of d9THC and some THCV). Billy was able to stop his other medication and, perhaps because of this and the reduction in his seizures, his cognitive and motor abilities improved markedly. But he was in the US while his mother and family were back in Northern Ireland, so they returned home and made contact with their GP. He was so impressed by Billy's transformation that he agreed to continue to prescribe the cannabis oil and supplies were obtained from an importer in the Republic of Ireland. When this became known, the local medical authorities threatened the GP with a charge of gross medical misconduct if he continued to prescribe what was an unlicensed medicine and an 'illegal' drug, so he was forced to stop. To prevent Billy's condition deteriorating his mother took him back to Canada for more supplies and then tried to import them into the UK, declaring them to Heathrow Airport customs officers. They were confiscated and Billy's condition rapidly worsened — his seizures returned, and he went into status epilepticus that required admission to St Thomas' Hospital Intensive Care Unit where he was sedated and ventilated. The public outcry in response to this cruel denial of a proven therapy, coupled with the real possibility of Billy suffering more brain damage or even dying, was profound. It persuaded the Home Secretary to give the Caldwell's a special personal licence to use cannabis oil, so his supplies were returned and his seizures stopped.

The Home Secretary also asked the chief medical officer to review the Schedule 1 status of medical cannabis and she stated that this was no longer appropriate because cannabis (or some components of it, such as CBD) were clearly a medicine. On November 1, 2018 cannabis products were moved into Schedule 2 of the MDA 1971. In theory this allows any doctor to prescribe them, but a caveat was included limiting prescription to specialists (or a GP acting under the instructions of one). There are no specified medical indications for medical cannabis in the UK so as long as the specialist has evidence of efficacy — which can come from published reports or personal patient testimonies — when a prescription as a 'special' can be offered.

However, the roll out of medical cannabis has been much slower than patients and parents had hoped. Still only three children with severe juvenile epilepsies are being treated, and many others continue to have multiple seizures because neurologists will not prescribe. A Drug Science conference on medical cannabis revealed there are several reasons for this. One is ignorance of the value of cannabis medicines and how and what to prescribe: few doctors have any training or experience in this field. Another resistance is to the reality that parents and patients lead this initiative rather than the medical profession. Some seem to fear that medical cannabis will lead to severe adverse effects such as psychosis and others retreat behind the argument that they don't like to prescribe 'off-licence.' Additionally, some pharmacists and clinical commissioning groups are resistant to opening-up what they see as the floodgates to medical cannabis prescriptions, and so are refusing to pay for them. Another significant challenge is obtaining supplies because currently all medical cannabis has to be sourced from overseas producers in Holland and Canada.

We must hope the situation will soon change for the better. Drug Science is contributing to progressing this by using a process developed by cancer researchers whereby small expert groups aligned to a specific indication, e.g. Tourette syndrome or adult epilepsy, are set up. These then conduct an open effectiveness study in this indication all using the same form of medical cannabis and all collecting outcome data in the same way. Something similar has already been developed for another ethically challenging treatment with another 'illegal' drug, ketamine, for depression. As such studies come under the ambit of clinical audit rather than a formal clinical trial they are much easier to set-up and much less expensive than traditional clinical trials.

In June 2019, Drug Science launched the initiative TWENTY21 in collaboration with the United Patients Alliance, the largest UK medical cannabis patient group. Our ambition is to have 20,000 patients in medical cannabis treatment trials by the end of 2021. In addition we have set up online training schemes for doctors and other health care practitioners and are developing the first training module in cannabis and endocannabinoids for medical students.

The conundrum of cannabis

There are multiple strains of the cannabis plant which differ widely in their many hundred constituent cannabinoids and terpenoids (the molecules that give the plant its distinctive smell). Of over a hundred different cannabinoids, most research to date has focused on the two which the plants produce the most of d9THC (Δ9 tetrahydrocannabinol) and CBD. The d9THC acts to stimulate cannabinoid 1 receptors, whereas CBD has a complex range of non-receptor actions. For example, although CBD has low affinity for CB1 receptors it can attenuate d9THC effects, i.e. cannabidiol can act as a functional antagonist of d9THC which can offset some of the more extreme psychological actions of d9THC (see below). CBD also enhances the brain's own endogenous cannabinoid, anandamide.

These two plant cannabinoids have a range of opposing effects on the human brain and behaviour. For example, d9THC acutely impairs learning, produces psychosis-like effects and increases anxiety whereas cannabidiol can enhance learning and has anti-psychotic and anxiolytic activity. When taken together, cannabidiol may ameliorate some of the harmful effects. A 2019 paper of ours showed using brain imaging that cannabidiol buffered the brain against some of the acute effects of d9THC. Previously Val Curran's team had shown that cannabidiol in cannabis acutely reduced the salience of cannabis-cues in recreational users. If cannabidiol can restore disruption to the salience network, this could be a neuroprotective mechanism which could explain its potential to treat disorders of salience such as psychosis.

The prohibition of cannabis for the last 40 years has led to dealers investing in more potent forms of street cannabis, where d9THC content has increased up to fourfold, with levels of over 15 per cent now common. This increase in d9THC means the plant is less able to produce cannabidiol so over this period there has been a significant reduction in CBD levels. Almost all cannabis sold in the UK is now high d9THC low cannabidiol variants (often called 'skunk'). What is worrying about this change in ratio of active ingredients in the cannabis sold is that it coincides with an increase in numbers of young people entering treatment for cannabis dependency. One approach to this problem is to consider giving CBD as a treatment for cannabis dependence and data on the efficacy and data supporting this idea has now been developed by Tom Freeman from the University of Bath. Another more politically challenging approach would be to adopt the Dutch model so allowing people to access less potent more balanced forms of the plant.

Medical cannabis

Despite extensive changes in policy on medical cannabis in over 20 countries, there is only a limited amount of definitive evidence on its medical benefits. The past 50 years of cannabis being in Schedule 1 has severely restricted medical as well as scientific research.

A couple of years ago the US Academy of Science and Medicine produced a detailed report with a wide range of research conclusions. In addition the cannabis charity representing self-medicating patients, the United Patients Alliance, in 2018 estimated that around 100,000 people are using medical cannabis for a broad variety of conditions. These indications range from (in order of self-reported use): pain, depression, anxiety, insomnia, arthritis, fibromyalgia, muscle spasms, irritable bowel syndrome, migraines, headaches and more. Many patients get therapeutic benefits from cannabis, especially in relation to pain alleviation and others report using cannabis as an alternative to prescription drugs. For many people, the medical use of cannabis improves their quality of life. Despite widespread 'illegal' use in the UK there are only four conditions currently supported by the medical authorities: spasticity associated with multiple sclerosis; intractable nausea and vomiting associated with chemotherapy; severe refractory (treatment-resistant) epilepsy, i.e. Lennox-Gastaut syndrome; and Dravet syndrome.

I believe one reason for the resistance of the medical profession in the UK to medical cannabis is the 'not invented here' syndrome. This is compounded by the fact that the main driver of use of medical cannabis so far has been the patient rather than the doctor. Patient-led treatment is not something most doctors are comfortable with as they feel it undermines their authority. I take the opposite view, and think medical cannabis is likely to be the last great innovation in addiction medicine in my lifetime and so something to be embraced not feared. Luckily, Drug Science also feels the same and together we hope to effect a change in practice soon. The TWENTY21 project mentioned above and outlined in *Chapter 7* will, we hope, provide just this impetus.

CHAPTER 11

And It Gets Worse! More Policy Madness with the Psychoactive Substances Act

The 27 May 2016 is a date etched forever in my mind for it was the day when the most repressive piece of legislation for over 400 years became law in the UK—the Psychoactive Substances Act of that year. This statute made it an offence to buy or sell any drug that has a psychoactive effect with the exception of alcohol, tobacco and caffeine which were exempted on the grounds of 'precedence.' It is important to realise that under the Psychoactive Substances Act 2016 it is not illegal to have some psychoactive substance in your possession for personal use, nor to have ingested one. But buying, selling or providing to others—even for free—is illegal and can attract a penalty of up to seven years in prison plus confiscation of assets under the Proceeds of Crime Act 2002. So, it's a pretty serious piece of legislation. But why was it brought in and was it warranted?

Despite pointed criticism from many senior members of the House of Lords and an embarrassed admission by the government lead in that chamber that alcohol was, in fact, more harmful than many of the drugs for which the Bill was introduced, it was passed easily in both houses because all major parties supported it. So now any drug that either 'stimulates or depresses the central nervous system' is illegal to buy or sell or even share with friends. This ban applies to substances that exist today such as nitrous oxide (laughing gas) and to any substance discovered in the future and deemed by the courts to be psychoactive. For the first time in UK history drugs are banned not because they are harmful but because they affect the brain. So, were a drug to be discovered that improved memory or intelligence or made people less violent or even made people more tolerant of each other, it would, *de-jure*, be psychoactive and so illegal.

I believe this is the worst law to control human choice and behaviour in the past 400 years. Not since the government of Elizabeth I passed the Act of Supremacy in 1559 has the state imposed such a severe control on the personal actions of its people. Then the ban was on believing in or practising the Catholic communion, now it's about changing the way you feel using drugs even though they may be harmless or even beneficial. The only redeeming feature of the Psychoactive Substances Act is that it does not make the use of psychoactive substances illegal, just their sale or purchase. Possession for personal use is still legal, but buying or supplying them is not.

What drove this draconian piece of legislation and why did so few MPs protest against it? The answer is complex but reflects a perfect storm of lies, disinformation and political machinations focused on newly emerging drugs — the so-called 'legal highs.' Since the banning of MDMA (ecstasy) young people had been looking for lawful alternatives, i.e. legal highs. Several came along and then were banned. The best known was mephedrone which in the late-2000s was widely used till it was banned by New Labour when they decided to pursue a 'tough on drugs' policy for the 2010 election. Even before the banning of mephedrone some other weak stimulants were available in 'head shops.' These were drugs such as methiopropamine, that were sold under the trade names of 'Bubbles' and 'Sparkle' usually to young people at weekends to increase their fun at clubs and parties. The effects of these stimulant were relatively mild, they were hardly more energising than a couple of cups of strong coffee. More importantly they were safe, with no reported deaths from their sole use.

But they became too popular, the head shops became a beacon for young people, especially when they added synthetic cannabinoids to their stock. Opposition rose in communities local to them who disliked the fact that 'drug users' were gravitating to their neighbourhoods even though the drugs they were purchasing were legal. Some of the more popular shops were closed down under public order legislation but this was too slow and complex a route for the media who began to wage a war on these shops, in a manner similar to the one they waged against sex shops on the 1970s.

In addition, the government became concerned by the continual innovation in new legal highs to replace ones they had banned. For example, once mephedrone was made illegal a close analogue, naphyrone came on sale. Though this was much less pleasant than mephedrone, and hence not popular, its mere presence sent some newspapers into further spasms of moral panic. So it too was banned, only to be replaced with other chemically-related compounds. This cat and mouse game also took place in the synthetic cannabinoid arena too and the media hysteria began to worry the government's drug advisors on the ACMD. Particularly prominent in whipping-up hysteria was the lobby group the Centre for Social Justice. The name seems to obscure the fact that this appears to be a well-funded (some from the US) right-wing Christian think tank that seeks to impose puritan, prohibitionist values on UK society. For several years they put out misleading data claiming that deaths from legal highs were rising rapidly year-on-year. Even though the Drug Science experts published data in the *Lancet* showing their data were incorrect they continued to misdescribe and exaggerate the harms of legal drugs. This body of misinformation was repeatedly presented in scaremongering terms and began to worry politicians. This fear of public disapproval overruled even the Home Office who agreed with Drug Science in pointing out that, in truth, legal highs were responsible for less than ten deaths per year.

The Tory government under David Cameron saw this as an opportunity to show the public that they too were 'tough on drugs' and asked the ACMD to review policy options. Their working group spent 18 months on this question and came up with a number of recommendations, one of which was to ban everything psychoactive—i.e. the idea of a Psychoactive Substances Act! With little public consultation this became the Conservatives' agreed solution and was put into their manifesto for the 2015 election. Labour, fearful of being accused by the Tories of being 'soft on drugs' and so losing leverage in the election decided they had to follow suit and put it into their manifesto. And even the Liberal Democrats, who really knew better, did the same to avoid 'soft on drugs' criticism.

The first Bill the Tories laid before Parliament after being elected was one to ban psychoactive substances. Faced with the problem that alcohol and tobacco were psychoactive, the Bill proposed to formally exempt them, and also caffeine, on the grounds of precedence, an as yet to be defined legal concept! No other drugs were exempted and *no* drugs other than these three are even mentioned in the Act. The Psychoactive Substances Act was therefore a truly bizarre piece of legislation, banning things that may not even exist! Despite this obvious absurdity (that Drug Science made clear during the debates) the Act was put into law because all three major parties supported it in their manifestos, so there was almost no opposition in the House of Commons. The more mature considerations in the House of Lords' debates that raised concerns about the Bill were overruled. The only issue that was properly debated was whether 'poppers' should be caught under the Act.

Poppers are air fresheners that contain amyl nitrites. These are inhaled by people to get high because in the blood they break down to the gas nitric oxide. This has profound effects in the brain (nitric oxide is in fact a brain neurotransmitter) and nitrites have been used for over 150 years to get people high. They were the drug of choice in the famous road trip on drugs in Hunter S Thompson's 1971 novel (later a film) *Fear and Loathing in Las Vegas*. So clearly nitric oxide is psychoactive in any sensible meaning of the word.

But several MPs, most notably the Tory, Crispin Blunt, wanted poppers exempted from the Act because it appears they used them personally. Poppers have become popular in the gay sex scene because the nitric oxide they produce, as well as giving a high, also relaxes the blood vessels of the penis, giving bigger and stronger erections. Nitric oxide also relaxes the smooth muscles of the anus making anal sex easier. This makes this kind of sex less dangerous in terms of abrasions and bleeding and so is thought to reduce the risk of HIV transmission. Blunt argued that banning poppers would increase the spread of blood born viruses, especially HIV. It was this latter argument that won the day and the government decided it wanted to exclude poppers (and other forms of nitrites, e.g. anti-angina medicines) from the Psychoactive Substances Act. But these drugs were clearly psychoactive—so how could they exclude them? Desperate for a 'get out of jail card' the government turned to the ACMD for help. The expert committee came back with a solution to the government's predicament: poppers via nitric oxide production are psychoactive but *only* because they dilate blood vessels going to the brain. This is true—poppers do lead to the dilatation of blood vessels—but nitric oxide also acts on many neuronal systems in the brain also. Nevertheless the government ignored the brain effects and poppers were excluded because their psychoactivity could be claimed as being an indirect effect (via increased blood flow) rather than a direct psychoactive action (via the brain).

Contorted logic perhaps, poor science undoubtedly, but the ACMD advice served its purpose and poppers were excluded (note *not* exempted) from the

Psychoactive Substances Act and so are still lawful. But are they? One remarkable feature of this new legislation is that *no* drugs other than the three exempted ones (alcohol, tobacco and caffeine) are mentioned in the Act! The fact that nitric oxide isn't mentioned in the Act means that it could still be illegal.

So, who decides whether a new drug is lawful or criminally unlawful, in common speech legal or illegal? Astonishingly the Act leaves this decision to a jury. The way the Psychoactive Substances Act 2016 works is that a police or customs officer has to suspect that a person is selling or buying an illegal psychoactive substance. They then make an arrest and the case is heard either by magistrates or in the Crown Court in front of a jury depending on perceived seriousness and the accused person's rights. Having been an expert witness in a number of these cases I can reveal the problems that this entails. In the Crown Court the 12 people who make up the jury have to decide if the substance is psychoactive or not. Given most jury members have no idea what the word psychoactive means, this is a real challenge for them. And when they discover that there are no examples of other drugs for them to compare with the drug in question they are even more bemused: how could a government enact a law banning drugs without any examples? They rapidly come to the conclusion the law is an ass. Which in this case it is. It is also scientifically dishonest as the attempted prosecutions of people selling another psychoactive gas, nitrous oxide, show.

Banning nitrous oxide — no laughing matter!

Nitrous oxide is the chemical name for laughing gas. This gas was discovered in the 1780s by two of our greatest ever chemists Joseph Priestley and Humphrey Davy. They noted it induced a state of good humour and called it 'laughing gas.' In the 1800s it was widely used recreationally with laughing gas parties being a popular form of entertainment. Early psychology researchers such as William James used nitrous oxide to explore the nature of consciousness and it is reputed that poets such as Robert Southey and Samuel Taylor Coleridge used it for inspiration when they could not get hold of opium.

In the 1800s, nitrous oxide's anaesthetic and analgesic (pain killing) properties were discovered, and it has been used as a short-lived anaesthetic ever since then. It is still a popular anaesthetic for childbirth pains and also for re-setting fractured bones and dislocated joints. Nitrous oxide is also used in catering because its odourless and so can be employed to froth up cream without altering its taste. In this use the nitrous oxide is usually obtained from a small aluminium canister ('a whippit'). Over the past two decades there has been a resurrection of interest in the experiential use of nitrous oxide using gas from whippits. One of these containers is used to fill a balloon and then the gas is inhaled from the neck of the balloon. A short lived 'high' or 'head rush' is produced that lasts one-to-two minutes, with full functional recovery soon after.

There are some good reasons for this resurrection of the recreational use of nitrous oxide. First, nitrous oxide was a true legal high — it was (and as we shall see later maybe still is) legal. Second, it is quite safe, much less likely to kill the user than some other drugs, e.g. opioids and alcohol. Thirdly, because it's a gas, it is rapidly breathed out so its effects are short lived which means users are intoxicated — and hence vulnerable to assaults — for just a short time. One benefit of nitrous oxide over alcohol is that they can safely drive within minutes of taking a dose. Moreover, there is no hangover, and this is the main reason why many people — and particularly footballers — choose to use it over alcohol. You can have fun at a party with either drug, but the next-day effects of an alcohol hangover can seriously damage your performance, whereas nitrous oxide has no carryover impact. It turns out that it's the use of nitrous oxide by football stars that got it banned.

The *Sun* newspaper, flushed with its success of getting mephedrone and other cathinones banned, decided to turn its attention to nitrous oxide. It gained access to mobile phone photos of players such as Raheem Stirling inhaling from a nitrous oxide gas balloon. He was within his rights to do this and indeed still is allowed to do this because personal use of nitrous oxide use was, and still is, legal. But the *Sun*, was seeking a story and wanted to get nitrous oxide banned. But even the *Sun* staff were smart enough to realise that to create moral panic about the use of laughing gas would make them look stupid as many of their readers, especially those who were mothers, would have used it without harm during childbirth. So, they decided they had to change its name to something much scarier and invented the term 'hippy crack.' Now this was something that would worry people especially those who knew how dangerous crack cocaine was and who remembered the hippies of the 1960s with their flares and tie-dye t-shirts! Scaremongering about the immorality of nitrous oxide use started and was taken up by other right-wing papers such as the *Daily Mail*. These chose to attack media celebrities such as Lily Allen whom the paparazzi photographed using nitrous oxide balloons.

This anti-nitrous oxide campaign worked and without any debate in Parliament the government decided that nitrous oxide was a psychoactive substance that needed to be banned. Almost immediately after the Act was brought in the police began invading music festivals and arresting people with whippits in their possession. This was probably the easiest piece of policing they had ever done because they just had to look for balloons and then find the person filling them and arrest them on the grounds that they were in possession of a prohibited substance with intention to supply. Even if there were no balloons, the clinking of the whippits in bags or backpacks made it easy to find people with some in their possession. The police made hay and at the Victoria Park Festival in East London in July 2016 so many people were arrested for nitrous oxide offences that the police in the park were told to stop because the local police stations were overflowing with suspects being charged! The arrests were so easy for the reasons I have already mentioned but also because at that time none of those selling the gas balloons knew that nitrous oxide might have been controlled under the Psychoactive Substances Act. There had been no public information campaigns warning users or sellers. Most people had never heard of the 2016 Act let alone knew it had come into force.

Along with many others such as the team at the drug charity Release, I objected to this heavy-handed approach. We felt prosecuting supply of nitrous oxide served no social or health purpose and decided to support those being charged. I began to act as an expert witness for the defence in a number of these nitrous oxide cases. My arguments were threefold:

1. Nitrous oxide is a medicine and medicines are exempted from the Psychoactive Substances Act.
2. The government could not prove that nitrous oxide was psychoactive as it hadn't conducted any studies on this. Worse, it didn't even know how to scientifically measure psychoactivity; and
3. Even if nitrous oxide was psychoactive then it would be excluded from the Act by the same reasoning as nitric oxide was excluded — its

effects were largely on blood vessels and blood flow to the brain, not directly on the brain.

The first defence was unimpeachable; nitrous oxide was a medicine and the first case at Southwark Crown Court in August 2017 was for this reason dismissed by the judge without a jury being sworn in. On the same day, a similar decision was made at Taunton Crown Court. But these cases were a year after the 2016 Act came into force and many people had already been convicted and imprisoned for nitrous oxide supply because they had been told by the police and their solicitors that there was no possible defence argument. Once these two successful acquittals came to be publicly known, then a whole slew of appeals were lodged against those prior convictions. The Crown Prosecution Service could see nitrous oxide escaping the Act and they asked the Court of Appeal to adjudicate whether using nitrous oxide for recreational purposes was legal, as it was a medicine. Unsurprisingly it dismissed these appeals and made it clear that the use of nitrous oxide as a medicine was legal *only* if it was being used in the treatment of a medical condition. So, the early convictions were upheld—and many people stayed in prison.

The other two defence arguments were still valid and I used them in a series of cases all around the country. I argued, as the defence expert psychopharmacologist, that nitrous oxide couldn't be proved to be psychoactive and, even if it was, then sellers should be excluded from prosecution based on the poppers/nitric oxide exemption. These court cases proved illuminating. We won some and lost some. But every jury was baffled by the idea that the responsibility to make the decision whether nitrous oxide is psychoactive or not fell to them. One can't blame them, usually complex scientific questions are decided by experts not juries, but the government delegated its duty with this Act.

Because cases were being won by my defence arguments the government decided to challenge my claim that since the effects of nitrous oxide were plausibly explained by changes in blood flow then it should be excluded from the Act like nitric oxide was. They pointed out that the Act itself didn't make any mention of direct or indirect effects. I retorted with a quote from *Hansard* made by Karen Bradley the Drugs Minister at the time that nitric oxide was being excluded. Her statement was based on the advice given by the ACMD that nitric oxide did not have a *direct* psychoactive effect on the brain. She said:

'Having given due consideration, the Government agrees with your advice and interpretation of the definition. We do so in the understanding that "poppers" have these *unique* [my emphasis] indirect effects. Our understanding is that this approach does not have any further implications for the operation of the Act and that other substances that the Act intends to cover are not affected. We remain confident that the psychoactivity of those substances can be established under the definition in the Act. We will ask law enforcement agencies to be guided by our agreement with your advice.'

Unfortunately for the government position it turns out that nitrous oxide also has significant effects on brain blood flow and its psychoactivity can plausibly be explained by these. The evidence suggests that probably more of the psychoactive recreational effects of nitrous oxide than those of nitric oxide can be explained by blood flow changes. Therefore, I argued, nitrous oxide should be exempt like nitric oxide is. This argument was then taken to the Court of Appeal in the case of *R v Chapman* ([2017] EWCA Crim 319) and that court's ruling was disappointing. It reported that in its judgement, for the purposes of the Psychoactive Substances Act, it was irrelevant whether the psychoactivity of a drug was via a direct or indirect action on the brain. Why—because the 2016 Act made *no mention* of direct actions.

So, the government had won—or had it? The implication of this appellate ruling is quite worrying for the users of poppers, because they now could face prosecution as the exclusion of nitric oxide also isn't mentioned in the Act! So, a policeman could arrest someone in possession of poppers and prosecute them under the Psychoactive Substances Act. It would then be up to a jury to decide and given the evidence I have outlined above they might find in favour of the Crown, that nitric oxide is psychoactive, and the person could face a jail sentence. The current (2020) Home Secretary, Priti Patel is now exploring ways to remove this uncertainty, by exempting nitric oxide from the Psychoactive Substances Act (which might well lead to nitrous oxide becoming exempted also!).

There is one other final twist in the tail of this bizarre Act. The decision of the Court of Appeal to ignore the Drugs Minister's statement and the ACMD's advice on indirect effects of nitric oxide was also challenged. A request was made to the Supreme Court for them to determine whether it was within the Court of Appeal's authority to ignore a recommendation of a government scientific expert committee (the ACMD) that was the basis of a major piece of legislation. As yet, no hearing has been held, but if they find against the appeal court's decision then a number of nitrous oxide convictions may have to be reviewed.

The Psychoactive Substances Act 2016 had some other perverse consequences. Parliament's ambition, indeed expectation, that it would close down the head shops has not transpired. Very few have gone out of business. Most now just sell drug memorabilia, cannabis smoking paraphernalia, t-shirts, etc. What has changed is that the sale of legal highs has moved from inside shops to the back streets, a harsher and more cynical black market. The head shop owners cultivated their customers as they wanted them to come back as regular weekly consumers whereas the back-street dealers have little customer loyalty, often being from distant cities.

Weak stimulants such as methiopropamine ('Bubbles' and 'Sparkle' (above)) are no longer available as they have been supplanted by more profitable, more addictive and more dangerous drugs such as potent synthetic cannabinoids (spice) and strong cathinones (e.g. pyrovalerone/monkey dust). Recreational users are now dying in ever greater numbers from these substances. As the Psychoactive Substances Bill was being debated I predicted this would happen if the Act went through, but as usual I wasn't listened to. Political expediency won again in the war on drugs and as we have seen many times before prohibition of one drug has led to more, not to less, harms. I wonder if governments will ever learn.

CHAPTER 12

Resurrecting Psychedelic Research with Magic Mushrooms

Since the US and United Nations bans on the recreational use of psychedelics in 1967 research on them fell to almost nothing. I now believe that this was the worst censorship of research in the history of science, as it effectively stopped research and clinical use dead. Before the ban, the US National Institutes of Health (NIH) had funded over 130 grants on psychedelics, 1,000 papers were published and the results were almost always powerful and positive. Since then the US government has not funded a single study, and until we started our research, nor had the UK government.

In this chapter I share the results of the fightback that for the past decade with my team led by Robin Carhart-Harris at Imperial College London, in collaboration with Amanda Feilding of the Beckley Foundation, we have set in motion. Our aim in doing so is to rectify this absurd—I would even say obscene—denial of scientific enquiry and potential therapeutic progress. We started with psilocybin, the active ingredient of magic mushrooms and asked one of the great unanswered questions in neuroscience—what goes on in the brain during a trip?

We chose to start with psilocybin, for a number of reasons. It is very safe—there have been no recorded deaths from it despite millions of people using it for millennia across much of the world. It is widely used as unlicensed medicine for the self-treatment of disorders such as cluster headaches, depression and obsessive compulsive disorders (OCDs). However, giving psilocybin in a brain scanner had hardly been done before and never using the intravenous (IV) route of administration. We were forced to use the IV route because this reduced the dose we needed to give, and hence the cost of the drug, by nearly tenfold. In reality, this was the only way we could afford to do the study. The 'illegal' status of psilocybin and other psychedelic drugs makes the cost of researching them extraordinarily high because of the mountain of regulations to be surmounted.

Because of the illegal status of psilocybin and the reluctance of conventional funding bodies to support psychedelic research our work had to be funded piecemeal. We had financial and intellectual support from our collaborator Amanda Feilding and her charity, the Beckley Foundation, and small donations from the Multidisciplinary Association for Psychedelic Studies (MAPS) and the Heffter Research Institute's associated charity. The rest of the money came from my consulting and lecture fees. These funds didn't cover the full costs of the research, and certainly not the medical staffing and imaging analysis costs. The only way we could cover these was from the generosity of the researchers themselves working for free on their days off, weekends, evenings, and nights. I coined the term 'guerrilla psychopharmacology' for this challenging, yet ultimately successful, approach.

The fact that psilocybin had never been used IV in a scanner before meant we had to perform pilot studies in a mock scanner to ensure that the drug was well enough tolerated in this confined space for the real imaging study to be viable. If the participants felt too anxious, they might refuse to continue the scan or be restless and move about, so reducing the quality of the data we would collect to useless. Pleasingly they tolerated it well in the mock-up and so the main imaging studies were conducted. However, in all our brain imaging studies so far, we have only used volunteer participants with prior experience of psychedelic drugs. This was to ensure that we minimised the risk of 'bad trips.' Also, this approach allayed fears of ethics and other regulatory committees that we might be introducing naïve volunteers to the use of these drugs, so possibly encouraging subsequent recreational use or self-experimentation with illegal substances. Of course, in the depression study I will describe below we had patients who were psychedelically naïve and in these we used a low test dose before the treatment dose to ensure that they could tolerate the drug. It turned out that even in the weird experience of a scanner (often described as having your head and body inside a washing machine) we had no significant problems with psilocybin, all participants tolerating it well. This is perhaps not so surprising given the fact that psilocybin is so safe that, in the UK, magic mushrooms were legal until 2005. They were largely used by teenagers and

20-somethings during the autumn growing season as a mushroom 'tea' usually, with 4–5 grams of dried mushrooms per cup.

At the time of our first studies there had been a couple of controlled studies of oral psilocybin showing its safety in treatment settings in the US. These were a nine person study of patients with OCD conducted in Arizona and a larger study looking at a single administration of psilocybin plus psychotherapy as a mood-improvement agent in mentally-well people conducted at John Hopkins University in Baltimore. Both showed efficacy with good safety and tolerability. Also, the Zurich group of Franz Vollenweider, the pioneer of modern psychedelic research, had used oral psilocybin in several pharmacological brain studies without ill effects. They had in addition conducted one imaging study of its actions on the brain metabolism using the technique of fluro-deoxy glucose PET. PET is a technique that uses radioactive tracers to measure aspects of brain metabolism and or function. This particular technique measures the activity of the brain over about an hour by charting its usage of glucose, the main energy source of the brain. The Zurich team found that brain activity was increased, especially in the middle brain structures, for the hours following the psychedelic drug treatment.

Another virtue of psilocybin is that it is relatively short acting, especially so when given intravenously when the effects last just for about 30 minutes, so even if people had a bad trip this wouldn't last long. In fact, virtually no-one in our research has had a bad trip, despite being in the unsettling claustrophobic environment of an fMRI brain scanner.

Perhaps most importantly, for getting ethical and university support for these studies, psilocybin is not LSD! It doesn't have the historical baggage of fear and misinformation that has been attached to LSD over the past 50 years in an attempt to deter young people from using it. Still, this research was challenging because of psilocybin's illegal status in the UK.

Turn-*off*, not turn-*on*

The first study we conducted was to give psilocybin in an fMRI scanner and look at changes in blood flow and memory. We gave a dose of saline (the placebo condition) and conducted scanning for 30 minutes; then we gave 2mg

IV of psilocybin and repeated the process—all the while the participants were lying still in the scanner. This is known as a fixed order design and we had to do it this way because we knew from anecdotal reports that psychedelics could have long lasting effects on people, so we reasoned these might reflect changes the brain in a way that it could appear to be due to the saline. The images were then subjected to a series of checks for quality, movement and other artefacts were removed, and the changes in brain activity under psilocybin compared with those seen in the saline placebo condition.

The first and critical question was whether the participants would experience the psychedelic effects in the scanner. The pilot data had suggested that they would, and they did, with many reporting strong effects. Some of these were simple hallucinations: classic bright geometric shapes, often rectangles or polygons, moving around the visual space, with an enhanced sense of colour and brightness. Also common were disturbances of visual stability with a sense of visual images moving. All these are typical of psychedelics. The classic alterations in the perception of time and space were also frequent. To a lesser extent spiritual and supernatural experiences were reported. Several reported their bodies disassociating and their self moving outside of the scanner.

We asked them to score their responses on a series of statements that covered a whole range of experiences that might be predicted to occur under the influence of psilocybin and which they had to rate from zero to ten. These statements ranged from some such as:

'My vision changed.'
'I saw things that weren't there.'
'My sense of time was altered,' etc.

They also included one statement 'I felt entirely normal' and this was the only measure that was scored significantly higher under placebo than psilocybin.

So far so good. We had produced the classic subjective effects of psychedelics even in the strange environment of the MRI scanner. And subjects were able to stay still enough for quality images to be produced. But what did we find in the brain? I can honestly say that the results were among the most amazing I have seen in a lifetime of science. They could not be a product of our deliberately misanalysing the data to 'find' what we were looking for because they were quite contrary to our original theories. Only once before had I ever had such a result of an experiment being completely opposite to that predicted. This was when we discovered the anti-benzodiazepines back in the early-1980s (See *Chapter 3*). From this finding I developed the scientific maxim that if your results are the opposite of those you predicted they are very likely to be true!

We had predicted that the visual hallucinations produced by psilocybin would be associated with an increase in brain blood flow (indicative of increased brain activity) in the visual regions of the brain. But activity in these regions was unaltered, so where did the hallucinations come from? The clue came from looking at activity across the whole of the brain. As in the visual regions we found no increases anywhere in brain activity, but in three regions there was a profound *decrease* in activity. Remarkably, the magnitude of the reduction in activity in these regions correlated with the scale of the psychedelic experiences. So, the old hippy call to 'Tune in, turn on, drop out' was completely wrong. The psilocybin trip experience was a turn-*off*, not a turn-on, of the brain!

These findings were so unexpected and remarkable that we decided that before publishing our results we should repeat the experiment. Replication is a critical and necessary element of the scientific process, though one that is frequently overlooked. So to find out if the localised turn-off of brain activity was a true finding we performed a second experiment but used a different type of fMRI technique, this time fMRI BOLD (blood oxygen level dependent) signal. This MRI approach measures brain activity more directly by the changes in the level of oxygen in the blood—the more brain activity the lower the oxygen concentration—as brain activity consumes oxygen. Again (and to our relief) we found that the only effect of psilocybin was to reduce brain BOLD activity and in the same three regions as we had found in the first experiment.

The regions of the brain turned-off by psilocybin were ones known to be important in the experiences of consciousness—the anterior cingulate cortex, the posterior cingulate cortex and the thalamus. The key regions for the hallucinatory and altered body states part of the psychedelic experience are the two parts of the cingulate cortex. These are not part of the sensory, motor or emotional systems, rather they are the key nodes in a network through which a large part of brain activity has to pass for the brain to act in a joined-up fashion. They are the key integrative centres of the brain.

The anterior cingulate cortex integrates feelings, motivation, emotions, and memories. The posterior cingulate cortex integrates the different forms of sensory inputs — seeing, hearing positional sense and touch. They are vital to the normal functioning of the brain and so these two regions themselves are strongly interconnected to each other. So, when you hear something the brain automatically moves the head and body to optimise the analysis of the sounds, checks the memory banks for prior exposure to it and then orchestrates an emotional as well as cognitive response. Then if the sounds are important, it lays down a memory with all these different elements encoded.

When the functions of these nodes in this network are disrupted, as in the case of psilocybin administration, this orchestration breaks down. The other different regions of the brain are still active, but not under central control. They are in effect 'doing their own thing' without central control. The orchestra analogy is a good one — the anterior cingulate cortex and posterior cingulate cortex act as the co-conductors of the brain's orchestra. When these conductors are not working in synchrony the different parts of the orchestra are not coordinated, so a different, unpredictable, series of discordant sounds from individual instruments are made. Instead of playing Bach the orchestra may end up producing jazz.

It now seems that the effects of psilocybin to produce visual hallucinations is due to the visual cortex being allowed to 'do its own thing.' In fact, the kind of images one gets in psilocybin visual hallucinations are just those predicted by our understanding of the way in which the neural columns of the visual cortex analyse their inputs from the eyes. Under psilocybin one is actually seeing the primary workings of the visual cortex which are normally not accessible because the integrative processes of the brain turn these simple images into the much more complex visual perceptions that we are used to experiencing.

Our participants said things looked strange and images seemed to move. This is because a normal visual image is a composite of integrated activity in many different brain areas that work together to create what we see. Your brain doesn't take a picture of what your eyes see, it makes a prediction of what the world is like from the complex electrical impulses that the retina in the eye sends via the optic nerve to the visual regions of the brain. One region of the visual cortex works out the location of the image in space, another region works out if there is movement and in which direction, another the colouring of the visual input and another one the shape in two-dimensions and three-dimensions. Then other 'higher order' regions integrate all these different regional outputs into what we 'see' as a normal visual image. Eventually memory and emotions are then attached to the final product. This is a majestic feat of integration of the computational power of the tens of billions of neurons that work in the visual system and associated areas such as the hippocampus. The truth is that the brain creates a reconstruction of what's out there in the world. Vision is a complex prediction based on electrical inputs from the eye.

We now believe that under psilocybin the connections between these multiple visual areas get disrupted. Images appear to move as the visual movement area is not properly synchronised with the others. Colours seem brighter as they are not dampened down by the content from other regions. Simple shapes are seen rather than just complex images as the usually perfect integration of the system is disrupted. The distortions of space and time are similarly produced by disrupting the integration of timing and location inputs mediated by the posterior cingulate cortex. This leads to the sense that some of the volunteers experienced their body sense changing and that they were beginning to merge with their surroundings. The posterior cingulate cortex is critical in defining a person's sense of inner self as distinct from the 'outer' world. If its ability to do this is impaired, then the *self-external* world distinction breaks down. In a few participants this breakdown of self-external world was so great that they felt as if they had left their bodies, or that their bodies had disintegrated. They felt that their body moved from inside the scanner and out into space for a while. For some this was associated with spiritual experiences. One even said during this out-of-body excursion that he moved through space towards a bright distant light and found himself bowing down at the feet of a deity.

There were also positive effects on mood. Some reported a profound inner peace and others just felt happy and energised. In a few cases there was the experience of mild synesthesia. This is detected to some extent by the scores on the statement, 'Sounds influenced the things I saw.' We explored this common and intriguing psychedelic phenomenon more in the LSD studies we shall come to in the next chapter.

Altering the 'self' circuit

Another way of looking at these effects of psilocybin comes from the understanding that the two nodes of brain integration, the anterior cingulate cortex and posterior cingulate cortex, are normally working closely together. These are two regions of cortex that are deep under the main cortex and which work in unison to form what is part of a recently discovered brain network known as the default mode network (DMN). The anterior cingulate cortex is located under the pre-frontal cortex and posterior cingulate cortex deep inside the rear cortex.

This DMN is identified by measuring the connectivity of these two regions under the placebo (saline) condition. With participants lying quietly in the scanner their eyes closed and not engaging in any outside tasks (the so called 'resting state') we identified activity changes in the anterior cingulate cortex and then looked to see which parts of the brain show changes in activity in the same direction as those in this region. It turns-out from our work, which confirms that of many others, that activity in the anterior cingulate cortex is strongly correlated with activity in the rest of the frontal lobe of the brain, and also with activity in the posterior cingulate cortex region. These regions together form the DMN, which we now believe to be the brain system responsible for the sense of self or ego. It is maximally active when we are *relaxed* and *introspecting*, e.g. when we are contemplating ourselves, planning the day ahead and reflecting on the past, i.e. when we are *not* doing things like speaking and moving. Hence its name—the *default mode* network.

Defining the DMN is not just a question of showing how the activity in its component parts change in synchrony together but also how these correlations are affected by changes in other brain regions and circuits. There are multiple other brain networks: the visual, the auditory, the touch and movement circuits, etc. In some ways the network most opposite in function to the DMN is called the task-positive network. This is active, e.g. when we are engaged in a sport. When this 'action' network is switched on then we don't want to be reflecting on our past or future so our DMN is switched off. But after the sports match when we are reflecting on how we performed, whether the tactics were right, etc. then DMN switches back on. The task-positive network dominates when we need to move or respond to the outside world and the DMN dominates when we enter our inner thought world. To that extent the DMN is a major seat of consciousness and self-awareness.

This form of reciprocal brain activity makes intuitive sense. When someone is thinking about themselves they are not usually engaged in active motoric behaviour or receiving lots of external sensory input (e.g. from a television or radio) so the task positive network is switched off and the DMN dominates. Conversely when the task positive regions are switched on then it makes sense that the DMN would be switched off. You would not want to be thinking about any profound regrets in your life whilst playing a vital game of football! In fact, such engagement with emotional thoughts is one of the main reasons why sports performance can falter.

Under psilocybin there is a dramatic change in the DMN. Psilocybin disrupts this network so profoundly that activity in the posterior cingulate cortex ceases to be synchronous with activity in the anterior cingulate cortex and other frontal regions. In effect the posterior cingulate cortex is functionally disconnected from the anterior cingulate cortex. The effect of disconnecting the DMN is to disrupt the inner organization of a person's sense of being and can transport them to other places or other worlds. In Freudian terms the DMN is that part of the brain that is responsible for the ego, the real person, all aspects of one's personality and identity, both good and bad. As we shall see later the DMN is overactive in conditions when people are over-engaged with a particular set of thoughts, such as a feeling of guilt or low self-worth in depression; of compulsive cleanliness in OCD; or craving in addiction. Conversely, the DMN can be disrupted in states of disordered thinking about one's self as can occur in schizophrenia. In fact, this disruption of the DMN produced by psilocybin may be a useful experimental model for schizophrenia as it can be produced fairly easily in the laboratory. What we don't yet know is whether conventional treatments for schizophrenia will block these effects. But this research is ongoing.

We think that the decrease in DMN connectivity explains many of the subjective experiences of psilocybin — the wandering thoughts, the sense of muddled thinking, vivid imaginations, and so on. Also, as we shall see later, upsetting persistent ongoing but unwanted activity of the DMN may be important in the experience of enduring positive mood that some of our participants reported.

Increased creativity under psychedelics?

Many people have reported that psychedelics can enhance problem solving and creativity. Perhaps the most famous was Kary Mullis, the Nobel Prize-winning biochemist. He was awarded his prize for his discovery of the technique called polymerase chain reaction (or PCR). Remarkably the insight to develop this technique came from LSD trips Kary experienced earlier in his life. To this day Kary asserts that scientists should use mind-expanding drugs like psychedelics to gain mastery of challenging problems. Later in the book we shall see how this is now being put into practice in some cultures through LSD micro-dosing.

Kary Mullis' assertion of the value of altering consciousness to solve difficult scientific questions reminds us of how, a century before, the German chemist August Kekule solved the benzene structure problem in an hallucinatory state. The benzene problem, of how to get six carbon atoms but only 12 hydrogen atoms, into a single molecule had baffled the world's top chemists for years. When falling asleep and entering a state of altered consciousness, probably a hypnogogic hallucination, Kekule saw the answer. The benzene molecule was not linear but circular, the two end carbon atoms joined-up to make a ring of carbon atoms, with two less bonds for hydrogen atoms. This insight was not only correct but proved to be the critical breakthrough in carbon chemistry on which the whole of modern organic and medicinal chemistry has subsequently built. That these major discoveries that revolutionised branches of science were made in hallucinatory states may not be as surprising as they seem when we consider the words of another scientific genius—Albert Einstein, who said 'No problem can be solved from the same level of consciousness that created it.' I often wonder what other scientific breakthroughs might have been denied or at least delayed by the ban on psychedelic drugs that was imposed in the 1960s.

How can a drug that switches off key nodes of brain function lead to an increase in creativity? The answer may be that, by disrupting normal thought patterns, new and more conceptually novel or radical thoughts and insights can be made. Our work with psilocybin shows that the changes produced by this drug work in that direction. This analysis is based on looking at the connectivity of a number of different brain regions using correlated changes in activity between regions as the measure of connectivity. In the placebo condition the brain has a number of preferred connection states (e.g. the left and right anterior cingulate cortex work closely together). The same goes for the left and right hippocampi and the right hippocampus with the right anterior cingulate cortex.

Using sophisticated statistical measurements our colleague Dr Enzo Tagliazucchi was able to identify the five most connected brain regions in the normal (placebo) state and then examine what happens to them under the influence of psilocybin. He found that the five most connected regions changed after psilocybin with the hippocampus-anterior cingulate cortex links across the two sides of the brain becoming more prominent and the lateralised connections becoming less so. In other words, the two hemispheres of the brain are more cross-connected under psilocybin than under placebo.

What such changes in connectivity may mean is that there is less emphasis on specific lateralised memory function in which the hippocampi work with the anterior cingulate cortex to produce; so there is more emphasis on cross-hemispheric brain integrative functions. A major impact of psilocybin is that *new connections* emerge that are rarely if ever found in the non-psychedelic state. For instance, both the left and right hippocampi are more likely to connect to both the left and right anterior cingulate cortices. In fact, multiple cross-brain connections are made under psilocybin which probably explains why so many people describe new insights into their past behaviours under this drug. They often relive significant memories of prior or ongoing problems and difficulties and get new more useful insights into their roles in them. Their brain is allowed to work in a different fashion under the influence of the psilocybin. It can explore different connections between memory and emotions and so new insights and understandings can develop.

To prove this analysis was correct we worked with another group of mathematicians to explore connectivity in a somewhat different way, but the findings were similar. Normally activity in one part of the brain is connected most closely to regions that are near to it in the brain — the so-called 'small world' scenario. Under psilocybin this local connectivity becomes less prominent and many more 'distant' cross-brain connections are made. I believe that this intense increase in cross-brain connectivity explains why so many new insights emerge under psychedelics; making connections between brain regions that may have been isolated for decades gives the possibility of old beliefs coming to be reviewed and new ideas emerging. It also provides the first imaging explanations for other psychedelic phenomena, such as synesthesia, where different sensory modalities cross-react or merge.

It is perhaps remarkable that these novel interconnections and insights are so well-remembered. The most significant and important insights made under the influence of psychedelics can continue to be used and even developed long after the drug is gone. Indeed, some say for ever, as the late Steve Jobs, the founder of Apple Inc. and one of the leading creative forces in the modern world discovered. He publicly announced that LSD was one of the five most important experiences of his saying,

'Taking LSD was a profound experience, one of the most important things in my life. LSD shows you that there's another side to the coin, and you can't remember it when it wears off, but you know it. It reinforced my sense of what was important—creating great things instead of making money, putting things back into the stream of history and of human consciousness as much as I could.'

The enduring nature of psychedelic experiences is what differentiates them from similar types of experiences that occur during dreaming. Dream contents, though often fascinating and emotionally laden, are rarely retained for a few seconds after waking, unless the dreamer is trained to write down or rehearse their content at once. The ability of the brain to remember psychedelic experiences tells us that the core processes for the laying down of memories are not affected by these drugs. Memory encoding requires sufficient activity of the neurotransmitter glutamate. This neurotransmitter is unaffected by psychedelics because they act on the serotonin receptor system so experiences under psilocybin can be encoded in memory.

The *level* of consciousness, how awake and how attentive we are, is determined by the relative balance between the neurotransmitters GABA and glutamate. Glutamate increases the level of alertness and GABA decreases it. Glutamate release is vital for the laying-down of memories. Drugs such as alcohol and benzodiazepines impair alertness and memory and cause sleep and amnesia by increasing GABA and, in the case of alcohol, also blocking glutamate. A rapid and pronounced surge of glutamate, probably also with a surge of emotion-related neurotransmitters such as noradrenaline, results in the powerful and entrenched factual and emotional memories seen in people with post traumatic stress disorder (PTSD). An excess of glutamate can lead to over-excitation of the brain and this can result in seizures (fits) that then take on a life of their own as they too have a memory trace that facilitates more seizures.

The meaning or content axis I think is driven by activity of the serotonin system probably through the 5-HT2A and maybe the 5-HT1A receptors on which psychedelics and other drugs such as MDMA act. Because serotonin receptor stimulation does not alter the level of consciousness or alertness, we can remember the experiences encountered under these drugs that can profoundly alter the nature and content of our thinking and feeling. Our own work has confirmed that after a single dose of psychedelics people do become on average a little more open-minded.

From these neuroscience insights we began to consider a possible role for psilocybin in depression and these studies with their exciting results are shared in the next chapter.

CHAPTER 13

Psilocybin and Depression

We have known for over 50 years that some case of depression are due to a deficit in serotonin and that drugs that enhance serotonin such as the selective serotonin re-uptake inhibitors (SSRIs) (Prozac and Seroxat for example) or monoamine oxidase inhibitors (MAOIs) (phenelzine) are effective anti-depressants. But as we learned in *Chapter 4* there are many sorts of serotonin receptors in the brain, so which ones does serotonin work through to lift mood?

One of the most remarkable aspects of the new research in psychedelics is the body of work coming together that shows they can produce enduring improvements in mood. This suggests that the 5-HT2A receptor may be a critical one for regulating depression. This line of work has also raised the possibility that, if indirectly stimulating these receptors by increasing synaptic serotonin using SSRIs works to lift depression, then maybe direct stimulation of these receptors with psychedelic drugs might also have anti-depressant effects. If so, then they might even be a treatment for some depressions that have not responded to more conventional therapy.

The first controlled scientific study on the mood-improving actions of psilocybin came from Roland Griffiths' group at the John Hopkins University School of Medicine. They developed a programme of psilocybin-assisted psychotherapy for people looking to improve their sense of wellbeing. These participants were given a day long therapy session under quite a high dose of psilocybin (30mg orally) with psychedelically trained therapists to help them work through their experiences. The control group got the same interventions and psychotherapy but instead of psilocybin they were given methylphenidate (Ritalin). This is a stimulant that is used to treat attention deficit hyperactivity disorder (ADHD) and was given as an 'active placebo,' a drug to produce some psychological effects in the control group so making it less likely that they would realise that they had not been treated with psilocybin.

In the psilocybin group there was a very significant improvement in mood and wellbeing for years after the treatment. In contrast, the control (Ritalin-treated) group showed little change in ratings. So, the psilocybin-psychotherapy session had produced a long-lasting improvement in mood and wellbeing as predicted. When the subjects were later asked to look back over their psilocybin session most reported it as having been of great significance to them. Remarkably, the majority of the psilocybin-treated group said it was one of the five most important experiences of their life—reminiscent of the comment we have already heard from Steve Jobs about his experience with LSD.

These data struck us as being so powerful that we decided to ask the participants in our psilocybin brain scanning studies about the effects of the drug on their mood over the next few weeks. Despite all of the drug effects being experienced while the participants were lying in a scanner and doing a variety of psychological tasks, some of them reported powerful improvements in mood, that in some cases lasted for several weeks after. Here is one description:

> 'Ever since [the scan I] have found it much easier to engage in the moment—to attend to the here and now; whether this be watching water in a fountain or sitting in science talks and meetings this morning. There were some fountains in Cardiff and the water was being blown by the wind, allowing the sun to highlight the spray. I could have watched it for ages—somehow the beauty was enhanced…Whatever it was, it has lasted—like the sun shining through the leaves this morning—it made me slow down my walk to work and enjoy the experience of it flickering over my face.' (Unpublished data)

Why would a short acting drug like psilocybin make people feel better or improve their mood for days or weeks? The simplest answer is that by stimulating the serotonin receptors in the mood centres of the brain it lifts depression. In other words, it could be a fast-acting version of other serotonin-acting anti-depressants. We know that the SSRI anti-depressant medicines take weeks to work because they act on the re-uptake of serotonin into neurons to increase serotonin in the synaptic cleft. Because they only indirectly stimulate the key post-synaptic serotonin receptors this effect takes time to build up due to compensatory adaptive mechanisms in the serotonin neurons that take a few weeks to be overcome. Another possibility is that maybe psilocybin is more powerful than serotonin itself at stimulating these receptors. Though this isn't the case in the test-tube, it is possible that the receptors in the brain are somehow different.

But our brain imaging work suggests there may be another rather different and more psychological explanation. As described in the previous chapter one of the key actions of psilocybin is to reduce the connectivity of the DMN. Recent brain imaging work in depression done in parallel with our pharmacological studies has shown that the DMN is over-active and over-connected in patients with depression. A second study went further as it showed that the *greater* the extent of connectivity in the DMN of depressed patients the greater was the degree to which they ruminated on their negative thoughts. Based on these data we now believe that depression is a state imposed on the mind by over-activity of parts of the brain that participate in driving the DMN.

This sense of imposition of depression on the mind of a sufferer is exemplified by this quote from the Scottish philosopher Thomas Carlyle:

'It was one huge dead immeasurable steam-engine, rolling on in dead indifference, to grind me limb from limb...having no hope.'

This gives us an insight into the remorselessly imprisoning mental process underpinning Carlyle's depression. He used a vivid metaphor which I think is a powerful description, i.e. of how patients with depression get locked into a thinking set just like a train is locked onto its rails (we sometimes call this 'tramline thinking'). In depressed people, thoughts and memories run a persistent path of negativity and guilt from which the patient cannot escape. Their negative thinking develops an autonomy of its own that immerses the person deeper and deeper in their depressive ruminations and prevents them being able to think about anything other than their depression.

By disrupting and quietening down the DMN we believe that psilocybin can reduce this negative thinking and break the ruminative process. Although the effects of the psilocybin only last for a few hours, the memory that the patient will have of being liberated from their ordeal of depression may be sufficient for them to stay liberated from the burden long after the psilocybin has disappeared from the brain. The experience under psilocybin may allow them to see another way of thinking outside of the depressive black box. This knowledge that their brain is still capable of normal thoughts can promote hope, and they can then work with these positive thoughts and memories to keep their depression at bay.

As we can see from the comments of Carlyle the experience of depression as a thinking process that comes from inside the brain and drives relentless thoughts is not new. If we go back to the Ancient Greeks they believed that depression was due to an excess of 'black bile'—a chemical that gave rise to the term melancholy (*melan* = black; *chole* = bile) which is sometimes still used by psychiatrists for severe depression, particularly in the elderly. The idea that depression was due to an excess of something negative or destructive to mood fell out of favour in the current period with depression becoming conceptualised more as a loss of positive mood, rather than an imposition of negative thinking. The reason for the current attitude to depression as being a loss of positivity derives from epidemiological studies that show, most frequently, that depression emerges from a 'loss event' (e.g. losing one's job or experiencing the death of a family member). This then led to the idea that depressed thoughts were a consequence of the relative loss of positive thoughts, an absence or deficit of activity in some 'good' mood centre of the brain. However, recent brain imaging research has shown that the idea that depression is something imposed on the brain was in fact correct. This important insight came from Helen Mayberg at Emory University in Atlanta whose studies have turned the whole field on its head. It now seems that depression is in fact a state of over-activity of a small part of the brain that drives people into negative thinking. This local over-activity can elegantly explain the description by William James of his own depression: 'It is a positive and active anguish, a sort of psychical neuralgia wholly unknown to normal life.'

Mayberg's studies have located this region that drives depression as being in part of the anterior cingulate cortex that is known as the subgenual region, and generally referred to as CG25. In these studies, the greater the activity in this region the greater the depression. In other words the CG25 is the brain region that drives depressive thinking. That region has been implicated in depression by a number of imaging studies and even one *post-mortem* study. It seems particularly altered in patients with a strong family history of depression. We now believe that over-activity in CG25 drives depression and also switches off the areas that are underactive in depression. However, not content simply to describe this localised brain abnormality in depression, Mayberg went on to properly test her theory. If she was right that CG25 activity did lead to depression, then it should be possible to lift depression by switching this region off. Working with neurosurgeons that had expertise in deep brain stimulation to switch off over-active parts of the brain in Parkinson's disease, she had them implant electrodes into CG25 in patients with resistant depression. Then while the depressed patients were awake and on the operating table the electrodes were turned-on and CG25 switched off. Some patients reported an almost immediate lifting of their depression whereas others responded more slowly.

These improvements in mood occurred in most of her patients and persisted for weeks and months as they continued to have electrical stimulation through the implanted electrodes just as is done with patients undergoing this treatment for Parkinson's disease. Since her pioneering study there have been many trials of deep brain stimulation for resistant depression and, although it doesn't work for everyone, in some patients the results can be life changing.

Although the deep brain stimulation trial was hugely important scientifically, Mayberg's discovery that CG25 was over-active in depression may be the more enduring legacy. Since then many studies of different treatments for depression have found that successfully overcoming depression requires a reduction in brain activity in this region. These include studies of anti-depressant drugs, cognitive behavioural therapy (CBT), and even (when it works) placebo. Another intriguing aspect of this research is that several fMRI studies have shown that deep meditation can produce similar effects to psilocybin in the brain. Work from Jed Brewer at Yale University has revealed that when highly experienced meditators get into the transcendental state their brain activity shows areas of decreased activity quite similar to that we found with psilocybin, particularly in the DMN. These changes in the post cingulate cortex would be expected to break down normal ego boundaries and so can explain the sense of 'oneness' with the world that is one of the main goals of this meditation.

The switching-off of activity in the anterior cingulate cortex that meditation produces probably explains the contentment and relief of tension that deep meditators enjoy. It also has implications for the new 'mindfulness' approaches to depression. Mindfulness is a technique developed from meditation that has become a popular new alternative psychotherapeutic approach for the treatment of depression. The key principle is that the patient trains their mind to ignore, or at least come to terms with, negative depressive thoughts rather than to actively oppose and try to suppress them. Brain imaging studies have shown that mindfulness training will dampen down activity in the anterior cingulate cortex just like other drugs and physical treatments of depression.

One interesting new approach being tested by the psychedelic research group at John Hopkins University is whether low (below psychedelic) doses of psilocybin might accelerate patients' abilities to gain the skills to accomplish deep meditation. Currently it can take years of regular daily practice for practitioners to learn how to switch off their brain centres sufficiently to achieve transcendence (the desired endpoint of meditation where one is detached from the present world) so most people give up along the way. If psilocybin or other psychedelics in low doses could facilitate this ability, then it's possible many more people could gain benefits from deep meditation. This is one of several new approaches that see psychedelic drug treatments as facilitating other more conventional approaches to mind improvement or psychiatric treatments.

The first psilocybin depression study

Our decision to use psilocybin to augment psychotherapy for resistant depression emerged from our imaging studies. It was obvious that one of the main actions of psilocybin in those studies was to produce a clear reduction in activity in CG25. We wondered if this might explain the beneficial mood reports that we got from some of our volunteers after their psilocybin experience. We then began to think that maybe if psilocybin could switch off this region in patients with depression then, perhaps, we could use psilocybin to treat this disorder.

Given the ethical and legal challenges that this approach was bound to face we decided to start with patients who had the greatest need of a novel unproven intervention — those with resistant depression. This was defined as those who had failed two conventional treatments with anti-depressant drugs of two different classes. Such patients represent up to 40 per cent of patients with depression since current treatments are not effective in everyone. We applied to the main UK funder for experimental brain research, the Medical Research

Council (MRC), for funds to conduct a double-blind controlled study and were both surprised and delighted when this was agreed. This was in 2012 and the project was only completed in 2018 due to the immense regulatory hurdles that working with 'illegal' drugs entails.

Still we persisted and we obtained ethical approval for the first phase of our trial which was an open label ('open label' meaning that both patients and doctors would know that psilocybin was administered) safety and tolerability study in 12 patients. Our local hospital ethics committee were so concerned about possible adverse effects of psilocybin in people with depression that they insisted on our doing an unprecedented six months safety follow up on these 12 patients before we would be allowed to then perform a proper double-blind controlled trial.

The open label trial had a test phase where each participant was given a 10mg dose of psilocybin first. This was because no-one had administered psilocybin to depressed patients who had never experienced a psychedelic previously, and we wanted to be sure that they would be able to tolerate the full treatment dose of 25mg that was given a week later. In fact all subjects tolerated the 10mg dose well, some hardly noticing it, so all received the full, presumed therapeutic, 25mg dose. Most, but not all of our patients had a strong response to this that lasted around four hours and many described it as a profound experience that changed the way they felt about themselves and their depression.

Both drug administrations were conducted in a quiet treatment room that we had made much more homely and welcoming than the usual sterile and impersonal medical out-patient clinic space, with subdued lighting, warm wall hangings and pleasant music. They had two psychiatrists or psychologists acting as therapists. These were present at all times to guide the patients through the experience and deal with any psychological or medical issues that came to the surface. The day after the treatment session the patients returned to the clinic and talked through their experience with their therapists. This process is called *integration* and is important for the patients to allow them to consolidate and maximise the insights and therapeutic processes that the psilocybin trip initiated.

We used standardised rating scales to measure the mood of each patient before and then at regular intervals after the treatment day. Most scored much lower on scales of depression at one day, and one and two weeks, after the 25mg dose—and for some this beneficial effect lasted for months. Overall, all but two patients met the criteria for recovery from their depression at two weeks, a remarkable outcome for people who had been depressed and resistant to treatment for many years. All had failed to respond to two standard anti-depressant drug treatments and one had tried eleven different drugs. All but one had tried and failed to respond to CBT.

For some people these effects wore off after weeks though in others they persisted for six months, a profound outcome for a single therapeutic administration of a drug. Because the results in the first 12 subjects were encouraging and there were no serious adverse effects the ethics committee granted us permission to continue the study with another eight subjects. This was to add statistical power to the brain imaging part of the study which was designed to find out what changes in the brain might be associated with recovery from depression. We wanted to see if the effects of psilocybin to lift depression had the same brain basis as those that are believed to underpin the therapeutic actions of anti-depressant drugs such as the SSRIs. The extra eight subjects all showed some response to the psilocybin in terms of reduction in symptoms, with one or two doing extremely well right up to six months.

As yet, we don't know why some people do well and have a prolonged therapeutic response and others have a less enduring effect. One factor may be the extent of the psychedelic experience, for the couple of individuals who had mild trips didn't seem to do as well. It may be that the psychological impact of the trip is important and those people who did well seemed to experience profound insights into the causes of their depression and achieve some mastery of these during the trip. Many of these accounts are now published and many are very moving.

One patient summed it up like this: 'My outlook has changed significantly. I'm more aware now that it's pointless to get wrapped up in endless negativity. I feel as if I've seen a much clearer picture.' Another said, 'My mind works differently [now]. I ruminate much less, and my thoughts feel ordered, contextualised. Rumination was like thoughts out of context, out of time; now my thoughts feel like they make sense, with context and logical flow'; and another said, 'The reset switch had been pressed so everything could run properly, thoughts could run more freely, all these networks could work again. It unlocked certain parts which were restricted before.'

Several used computer analogies: 'I felt my brain was re-booted, I had the mental agility to overcome problems.' 'It was like when you defrag the hard drive on your computer, I experienced blocks going into place, things being rearranged in my mind, I visualised as it was all put into order, a beautiful experience with these gold blocks going into black drawers that would illuminate and I thought my brain is bring defragged, how brilliant is that!'

One common experience of those who had good outcomes was that they had a greater sense of 'connectedness' with nature and others after the trip. '[After the dose] When I went outside, everything was very bright and colourful and it felt different. I noticed things I didn't notice usually, the leaves on the trees and the birds, small details'; and another, 'A veil dropped from my eyes, things were suddenly clear, glowing, bright. I looked at plants and felt their beauty. I can still look at my orchids and experience that: that is the one thing that has really lasted.'

These improvements in perception could be enduring, so for example one person said six months later, 'Things look different even now. I would look over at the park and it would be so green, a type of green I'd never experienced before. Being among the trees was incredible, like experiencing them for the first time, so vibrant, so alive.'

For some patients, the experience was so intensely felt during the trip that they struggled to put it into words, but were able to do so later as one recounted their experience of the trip: 'I was everybody, unity, one life with six billion faces, I was the one asking for love and giving love, I was swimming in the sea, and the sea was me'; and another, 'Like Google Earth, I had zoomed out, I was absolutely connected to myself, to every living thing, to the universe.'

Two patients had experiences of feeling the presence of God: one said, 'Not God in some dogmatic way, a God-like archetype within your psyche, that is real and within you. I know this exists, I directly experienced it. I was suddenly taken in a rapture and I was floating in mid-air, with my eyes wide open and my mouth open, completely in a state of awe and ecstasy. It's a very powerful message to take away.' The other explained, 'Then I felt the presence of God: I have always thought that he was a man because of the way I was raised, reading the Bible, but it felt like a female energy.' Another patient described a female 'ancient being' who, although not referred to as God, was 'omnipotent and unconditionally loving.'

Some others saw religious imagery during the dose, such as temples and Hindu gods. One said at the peak of the experience, 'I was Shiva, dancing.' For other patients, although a spiritual principle was not specifically declared they described a powerful feeling of 'love' as a strong supernatural force. Such mystical experiences have been reported in other studies where psychedelics have been used to help people overcome problems and psychiatric disorders. For example, the John Hopkins group found that what they call 'mystical' experiences were predictive of a good response to psilocybin when used in psychotherapy and for smoking cessation. Whether such experiences simply reflect a bigger drug effect or whether they are a manifestation of a state of mind that is more amenable to producing fundamental changes in outlook is a critical question and something we are still exploring.

One way of looking at this issue is to consider the impact of the psychedelic drug treatment in terms of the size of the positive psychological experience under the drug, which we have called the 'peak' experience. We use this term to avoid any religious connotations though for some people this experience will be religious in nature. For others it will be more mystical or spiritual. We measured the magnitude of peak experiences using a scale designed for this specific purpose—the Altered States of Consciousness Scale—and found that the more patients scored on this then the better was their anti-depressant response. Importantly, the correlation between depression outcomes was significantly greater for peak experience scores than for other major effects of psilocybin, specifically changes in visual or auditory perceptions. Anxiety during the treatment had a negative relation to good depression outcomes, a finding the John Hopkins group had made previously. Taken together our findings suggest that the quality of the psychedelic treatment experience—the trip—is important in the therapeutic outcome and we are now working out how to maximise this in future trials and treatments.

Another unknown is why some of our patients stayed well for a long time whereas others had a shorter duration of response. By three months about half had maintained their good response with about a quarter in full remission (wherein their depression had completely disappeared). But the other half had slipped back towards their prior state of low mood, though only one was worse than before treatment and only slightly so. We could find no relation between the effects of the psilocybin and outcome other than that the more anxiety during the psilocybin session the less good was the outcome. This finding is making us wonder if in future studies we might give an anxiolytic drug such as a benzodiazepine along with the psilocybin to help minimise this effect.

It is perhaps not surprising that some people's depression can't be remediated by just a single psilocybin treatment. For many people, depression is a mind state that starts with abuse in childhood and persists for the rest of their lives. We know that children tend to believe that they have more effect on the world than they really do. So, when things go wrong, even if this is due to abuse from parents or other adults, they tend to think it's their own fault: they blame themselves. This is the early form of depressive thinking we think gets set in childhood and so sets the tone of their emotional life once they become adults. Depression becomes the normal thinking state, the default position so to speak, and breaking free from this is difficult. Psilocybin treatment may disrupt this and allow a period of normal mood but this underlying tendency to depression will gradually re-exert its dominance.

The implications for future treatments with psilocybin are that some people may require top-up doses every few months or years to maintain a state of non-depression, but for many this might be preferable to taking anti-depressant medicine every day.

What does psilocybin do to the depressed brain?

So, what happened in their brains to explain this recovery? We were able to perform brain imaging with fMRI before, and the day after, the treatment with the 25mg dose of psilocybin (when the effects of psilocybin were still present as an 'afterglow'). In the patients where we used the standard measures of resting state connectivity, we had shown them to be profoundly altered during psilocybin and LSD trips and also added in was a measure of subconscious brain reactivity in the form of amygdala responsiveness to fearful faces.

The amygdala is a small brain region tucked under the frontal cortex that coordinates subconscious responses to fear and orchestrates escape behaviour before threats even get into consciousness. This role of the amygdala is easily demonstrated in the fMRI scanner by showing people pictures of other people's faces who are showing fear themselves—the so-called fearful faces paradigm.

This has been widely used for decades as a means of producing activation in the amygdala during fMRI scanning. Moreover, people with depression tend to show greater activity when depressed than when recovered and anti-depressant drugs—especially those working on the serotonin system (SSRIs)—attenuate this activity. There is a widely accepted theory that the primary effect of these drugs is to attenuate the excessive amygdala reactivity. This blunting of amygdala responses occurs very early in treatment, after just a day or two, and initiates the anti-depressant effect. The anti-depressant-induced amygdala blunting in depressed people reduces their distress so allowing them to respond more normally in interactions with other people which previously were stressful and threatening. Over weeks this reduction in stress reactivity leads to the patients increased engagement in real-world activities which is rewarding and so this then translates over time into the lifting of the depressed mood.

Based on this well-established theory of SSRI action we predicted that those patients who had recovered from their depression following the psilocybin treatment would show reduced amygdala activity also. However, we found exactly the opposite; that the day after the psilocybin treatment there was *enhanced*, not reduced, amygdala activation to fearful faces. In fact, there was also increased activity in response to happy faces as well. This result turns on its head the prevailing view that amygdala reactivity has to be turned down to achieve an anti-depressant effect. We now believe that the psilocybin data suggest there are two different ways in which serotonin receptor acting drugs can lift depression. The first and traditional way is by the SSRI-induced blunting of amygdala reactivity that is mediated by increased activity at the 5-HT1A receptor. This leads to resilience against threats, and by buffering people against stress it protects against further episodes of depression, so long as the medication continues to be taken. The other approach is via stimulation of the 5-HT2A receptor—for instance, with psilocybin. This we believe leads to a breakdown of the rigid thinking patterns that allow the patient to reframe the problems that led to the depression in the first place and so overcome them. The increased cognitive flexibility that psychedelics allow during and maybe after the trip may allow patients to develop their own mastery of their problems and so overcome—rather than be protected from—depression.

What of the tramline thinking process that underpins depression as described by Thomas Carlyle? Does psilocybin disrupt this? Our imaging data showed that there were significant alterations in blood flow and connectivity of the brain following the psilocybin treatment. We found decreased brain blood after psilocybin which in the amygdala bilaterally correlated with the reductions in depressive symptoms on that day. This makes sense in that one would expect improved mood to result in a less stressful state and so lower amygdala activity.

We also found some reductions in connectivity within elements of the DMN as predicted. In particular, a decrease in connectivity between the prefrontal cortex and the hippocampus predicted treatment-response at five weeks. However, rather unexpectedly, we found that some elements of the DMN showed *increased* integrity post-treatment that also predicted outcome. Specifically, we found increased connectivity between the subgenual pre-frontal cortex (PFC) and the bilateral inferior lateral PFC circuit of the DMN greatest in those who maintained treatment-response at five weeks.

My own view is that this circuit is a key switch in the brain that controls the nature of mood. In depression, negative thinking and memories enter and dominate consciousness. Recovery by psilocybin doesn't eliminate these thoughts or memories but it switches thinking away from them to the 'normal' world of more positive memories. The pathway between the lateral PFC and the subgenual cortex may be the switch mechanism. To put it simply, therefore, it seems that psilocybin is producing a series of different effects on the brain. Whether one of these is determinative of the outcome, or whether all need to occur to produce an anti-depressant effect, is not yet clear. In the next psilocybin depression study we plan to conduct more imaging work, but this time we plan to image the brain when the patients have their main anti-depressant effect—at four-to-six weeks—and we will also compare the impact of psilocybin with that of the most selective SSRI escitalopram.

Our first psilocybin depression study confirmed our expectation that psilocybin was remarkably successful as a treatment for depression, and, equally importantly was safe in patients with depression. But it was an 'open' study, in that everyone, both patients and doctors, knew that they were being given an active drug. It is well-known that this open design is likely to bias the result in favour of a positive outcome. What we plan to do next therefore is to conduct a conventional double-blind study in which patients are randomised to either a psilocybin treatment or to a placebo. The time and complexity of conducting the open label safety phase meant that almost all of the MRC grant had been spent before we could start on the double-blind study. We were therefore quite fortunate that the Mosley Foundation stepped in to support this next phase that started in 2018 with results due in 2021.

This new study (which we call Psilodep2) compares our 25mg dose of psilocybin with a low dose (equivalent to a placebo) but also compares the impact on mood and brain functions of the psilocybin trip with that of the gold-standard SSRI—escitalopram (10mg increased to 20mg after three weeks). We can therefore compare the efficacy of psilocybin with escitalopram in patients and use fMRI to explore our theory that different brain mechanisms underpin the therapeutic effects of these very different treatments. Preliminary results from the clinical trial are now available and show that psilocybin works faster and better than escitalopram on the majority of outcome measures. The brain imaging results are being processed.

One final point needs to be made on psychedelics and mood; even a challenging trip can result in improvements in mental state. This research outcome finds support in the reports of many people who engage in ceremonial or even treatment ceremonies with plant products such as ayahuasca, and particularly ibogaine, who comment that although the actual trip can be frightening and unpleasant they often emerge feeling far better. This is not just the effect of recovering from a tough experience for they often notice an enduring sense of wellbeing and inner harmony that lasts for months or even years which makes the transient discomfort of the actual bad trip well worthwhile. Perhaps these reports are not so surprising if we consider that it is highly likely (though not easy to study) that the same switching off of the DMN occurs whether one has a good or bad trip. Even during a bad trip, tramline thinking will be disrupted and new thought connections may be made under the influence of the drug that can continue beyond the trip.

CHAPTER 14

A General Theory of Psychedelic Actions — Imaging LSD and DMT

In many ways LSD is the Godfather of all psychedelic drugs. It is the most potent by far of the various classic serotonin 5-HT2A receptor agonist hallucinogenic drugs and many users say it produces the most useful and insightful 'trips.' In the 1950s and 1960s LSD had been extensively studied with more than 1,000 papers reporting its actions in multiple human studies. This makes the body of scientific literature on LSD much greater than that of all other psychedelic drugs put together. I believe it also is the only drug to be banned in the west because of its effects on social attitudes rather than because of honest concerns about its potential harms to health. The impact of LSD to change the perspective of the younger population was seen as too threatening to the western Establishment, particularly that of the US. The history of LSD and the Establishment's response to it are well described in Jay Stevens' *Storming Heaven: LSD and the American Dream* and Martin Lee's *Acid Dreams: The Complete Social History of LSD.*

The story of how the Swiss chemist Albert Hofmann, working for the Sandoz pharmaceutical company, accidently discovered LSD is one of the most remarkable examples of serendipity in science. Hofmann was making chemical derivatives of ergot, a migraine medicine, to find improved treatments. In 1938 he made a series of different compounds based on the core active chemical of ergot lysergide. One of these was LSD-25 a derivative with two ethyl amide groups attached to the lysergide molecule — hence the name lysergic acid diethylamide or LSD. The 25 means it was the 25th derivative of lysergide he had made. Such chemical substitutions are the bedrock of medicinal chemistry as they produce new compounds, often with different pharmacology to the parent, and so can be patented. The two ethyl-amide attachments make the lysergide much more stable and explain the long half-life of LSD in the body.

At the time Hofmann didn't know that LSD had peculiar and different properties to the other lysergide derivatives, but one day, several years later in 1943, when revisiting this series of compounds he accidentally swallowed a tiny amount when pipetting a solution of it. His description of the effects is now legendary. Hofmann recounted the first LSD psychedelic experience like this:

'I sank into a not unpleasant intoxicated-like condition, characterised by extremely stimulated imagination…perceived an uninterrupted stream of fantastic pictures, extraordinary shapes with intense, kaleidoscopic play of colours. After some two hours this condition faded away.'

From that point on the unique effects of LSD on consciousness were apparent to all who tried it. Sandoz were persuaded by Hofmann that this was a revolutionary compound that could unlock the secrets of the brain and also provide novel treatments for many severe mental disorders, such as depression, anxiety and addiction. We need to remember that at this time in the late-1940s none of the currently used psychiatric treatments had been discovered and for most people treatment for psychiatric problems was limited to being sedated with barbiturates or just locked-up in an asylum.

Those few scientists that start to work with 'illegal' drugs usually give up when they realise the cost and burden of doing this research and just get on with other, easier projects. The proof of this premise is that since LSD was controlled under the UN there were no studies for nearly 50 years. The good news is that in the past couple of years more extensive trials of psilocybin and MDMA have been carried out and now the regulators seem to be becoming more open to considering their therapeutic potential, and the effects of LSD in the brain have been revealed. The situation is now beginning to change as our group and two in Switzerland have worked through the regulatory maze and begun studies, three of which have been reported in the past year. That two of the three groups are from Switzerland is appropriate since LSD was discovered there, and the Swiss have always valued pharmacological research more than most other countries. In the UK only our group has persevered to put psychedelics back into brain science.

After many years of planning and application writing, my psychedelic research group at Imperial College London, led by Robin Carhart-Harris and working with the Beckley Foundation, eventually gained permission to do the first ever brain imaging research study on LSD. As with the psilocybin imaging studies (*Chapter 13*), we also worked with the Cardiff University imaging group using both their functional magnetic resonance imaging (fMRI) and magnetoencephalography (MEG) expertise. The longer duration of action of LSD compared with that of psilocybin meant that we are able to scan each subject with an fMRI then an MEG scan on the same day during the same LSD 'trip.' This kind of multi-modal imaging study is rarely done in neuroscience as it is so difficult to organize, but it has the great advantage of allowing the two quite different but fully complementary imaging modalities to offer an internal validity check of each others' results.

As with the psilocybin studies we gave the LSD intravenously. This was to minimise the cost of the drug (though the savings with LSD are less than those with psilocybin as the IV dose is not much less expensive than the oral dose), to shorten the duration of the drug's effects to a more manageable six-to-eight hours, and to provide a more consistent time of onset of drug effect to optimise the scanning protocols. To choose the right dose we first conducted a pilot study outside the scanner starting with a very low dose and building up the dose in subsequent participants until we found one that produced a powerful but manageable 'trip' that would be acceptable for use in a scanner.

The pilot worked well. Not only did we identify that the dose of 75 micrograms was optimal but we were also able to show it was safe in that there were only minor effects on blood pressure and heart rate. Importantly the participants were still able to engage with the psychological tasks we set them. These pilot tasks showed that LSD increased mental flexibility and music appreciation, two areas we wanted to explore in more detail with imaging. They resulted in the first human LSD paper from the UK in over 50 years being published in the scientific journal *Psychopharmacology* in early 2015. The block on LSD research had been broken! As one of the anonymous referees of this paper said, 'This was a long-awaited resumption of psychedelic research.'

However, the key question was: 'What would we find in the imaging study?' Would the LSD administration produce a different set of brain activity than that seen on the saline placebo day? Would our theory derived from our psilocybin studies — that psychedelics *turned-off* rather than turned-on the brain — be replicated? As replication using another drug or technique is a critical element of the scientific process this was an exciting, if somewhat nervous, moment for us. The different technique-specific analytical expert groups worked through the data for several months, cleaning out the parts that were artefacts due to excessive head movements or technical recording errors. Brain images made with the different techniques had to be co-registered to the same MRI anatomical coordinates to allow cross-comparisons between subjects. Eventually after several months of this pre-processing we had a solid data set that could be subjected to statistical analysis and then the code could be broken and the LSD day effects could be compared with those of the placebo day.

To our relief the core findings were the same as with psilocybin but more pronounced and significant. There was no net increase in brain activity under LSD, just altered functionality in the same regions as we had seen with psilocybin. Also, the key subjective effects correlated with the alterations in activity as with psilocybin. The majority of our participants experienced a degree of ego-dissolution and this subjective state was significantly correlated with the reduction in DMN coupling, as we had previously shown with psilocybin. Again, the posterior cingulate cortex was seen as central to the ego-dissolution experience, as the more this region became uncoupled from its usual network the stronger the experience of ego-dissolution.

Another clear finding under LSD was that many of the different networks of brain activity that are normally quite segregated from each other became much more overlapping under the psychedelic. This de-segregation mimics that found with the visual network and gives more examples of cross-modality interactions. Under LSD we found that most of the usual brain functional networks became less discrete and synchronised. The greater the degree to which these began to break down the greater the psychedelic experience. But also, as these networks became less individualised the greater the connectivity between different networks was apparent. This hyper-connectivity state helps explain several key features of the LSD state. For instance, we can understand the nature of synesthesia because regions that don't normally 'talk' to each other are able to do so under LSD. So we can 'see' colours in sounds because the visual and auditory cortex talk to each other under LSD whereas they do not normally.

Also, the powerful ability of LSD to lead to novel insights into a person's past behaviour can be understood because traditional blocks to thinking about these sensitive issues are broken down under the drug. We don't yet know if it's the breakdown of the usual partitions to thinking that allow new ideas to come together, or whether it's the hyper-connectivity that encourages new insights. It may be both are important, perhaps the breaking-down of repression is the first stage that allows hidden or suppressed memories to be accessed again. Then the new connectivity facility may allow new insights and different understandings and interpretations to be made that help us resolve issues long hidden and blocked.

It seems that one of the reasons people often report major insights under psychedelics is because this state of increased connectivity allows the linking of current and past visual and other memories with feelings and insights. In some people these connections can be completely novel and so produce life-changing insights. One of the most scientifically influential such experiences must be that of the Nobel Prize winning chemist Kary Mullis we touched on in the previous chapter. When searching for a way to measure DNA, he took LSD and his serpentine hallucinations led him to discover the mechanism of decoding the nature of DNA using the polymerase chain reaction (PCR). DNA is a complex coiled molecule that when disentangled resembles a helix of snakes. Just like many ayahuasca users who see snakes during their experiences, Mullis saw snake-like portions of DNA unravelling and replicating during an LSD trip. He then realised that if he could find a way of doing this in the test-tube he would be able to much more rapidly decode DNA. So, he sought out and found an enzyme method that would do this using polymerase. With this he invented and developed the polymerase chain reaction for which he was awarded the Nobel Prize in 1993. The PCR is now a cornerstone of modern biology and allows us to test for anything from bacteria in wounds to horse-meat in our hamburgers. PCR allows us to analyse tiny samples of DNA from different species, or even single cells, including those from dead species such as mammoths or insects.

One of the more remarkable discoveries we made in our LSD study was the nature of the complex visual hallucinations it produces. We found that the more of these a participant experienced the greater was the extent of connectivity between the visual cortex and the other parts of the brain. As we learned about the DMN earlier in this chapter, the frontal regions of the brain tend to connect to the anterior and posterior cingulate cortices and the activity in this network is usually distinctly segregated from those of the visual and other sensory regions. In the normal state where the brain relies on 'small world' local connectivity the visual cortex tends to talk to itself with limited interactions to other brain regions. Under LSD there is a vast increase in connectivity between the visual cortex and many other brain regions, the small world is opened up and a large-world network emerges that mimics the sense of mind-expansion and universe-engagement that some participants experienced.

Another powerful example of the effects of LSD is its impact on the music-appreciation network. We found this became significantly more linked to the visual network under LSD. This probably helps explain the experience or sensations of synesthesia, where people can 'see' music or 'hear' colours. It also helps make sense of why music is often reported to be a powerful means of enhancing the psychedelic experience and is such as valuable element of psychedelic therapy. Music may open up more connections in the brain. For these reasons in our psilocybin depression study we used a special music soundtrack created by one of our PhD students Mendel Kaelen. This was used through much of each therapy session to enhance the psychedelic experience.

The MEG results conformed to the effects we had found under psilocybin—a significant reduction in the power of the electrical activity across the whole frequency spectrum. The power is a measure of the synchronicity of neuronal activity in a brain region. The more the synchronicity of the brain was switched down the more the subjective effects were experienced. The decrease in power was particularly apparent for the regions of the DMN where a global decrease in power, particularly in the posterior regions, was found to correlate with ego dissolution, just as with psilocybin. Similarly, in relation to visual hallucinations the greater the power decrease in the visual cortex the greater these hallucinations were. Also, the scale of the MEG changes closely correlated with those also seen using the fMRI imaging. This helped in verifying our conclusions that these effects of LSD were due to a turning-down of synchronised brain activity in these key consciousness-controlling regions.

Is the brain an instrument of controlling the mind?

Aldous Huxley experienced a state of *mind-opening* when he used psyche-delics — first mescaline and then LSD. From his education at Oxford as a student of English literature he found the perfect description of these effects in the writings of the 18th century mystic, poet and artist William Blake. Hux-ley used this quote from Blake's 1793 *The Marriage of Heaven and Hell* to make sense of the psychedelic experience:

> 'If the doors of perception were cleansed every thing would appear to man as it is, infinite. For man has closed himself up, till he sees all things thro' narrow chinks of his cavern.'

These two sentences contained so compelling an insight into the effects that psychedelics had on his mind that Huxley used the first on the title page of *The Doors of Perception* (1954, Harper Torch) which gives a comprehensive account of his psychedelic experiences. It in turn gave the name to a rock band — 'The Doors.' Huxley concluded that as psychedelic drugs could 'open up' the mind, the mind was therefore normally in a 'closed' state or at least one restricted in view through only a chink in the cavern. To explain this state Huxley came up with the hypothesis that 'the brain is an instrument for focusing the mind.' Our imaging studies have shown that both Blake and Huxley were correct, the brain does limit the mind and psychedelics expand the mind by opening the doors of perception. They do this by breaking down the constraints imposed on consciousness by key regulatory regions such as the posterior cingulate cor-tex and the DMN.

One other perspective on this hypothesis, that the brain limits perception of the world, relates to the situation in depression. The brain processes that drive depressive thinking constrain the depressed person to seeing just a 'depressed view' of life. When they are looking out of the 'chinks of their cavern' instead of seeing a few clouds and blue sky, as we non-depressed people might, they are forced to look into an aspect far more tempestuous. We now think that one way in which psilocybin might lift depression is by opening the chink in the direction of normal rather than abnormal views of the world.

Finding the entities? Ayahuasca and DMT

Having conducted groundbreaking imaging studies with psilocybin and LSD we have now begun to explore the impact of a third popular psychedelic—N,N-dimethyltryptamine (DMT). This is the active ingredient of the plant-derived drink ayahuasca. The plant cocktail's psychedelic effects were initially discovered by native tribes in the Amazon basin and it is now being used in many western countries as a sacramental drink in religious and experiential sessions, even though it's illegal in most western nations. Studying ayahuasca is difficult because of the uncertain and variable composition of the plant material and its preparation means that getting a standard dose for scientific research is very difficult, though the late-Professor Jordi Riba and his team in Barcelona have overcome this challenge and conducted brain imaging studies with ayahuasca mixtures.

However, the active ingredient DMT is available as a research chemical, even though its tightly controlled as a Schedule 1 drug, along with LSD and psilocybin. Rick Strassman started DMT research back in the 1990s, and popularised his findings in the book *DMT: The Spirit Molecule: A Doctor's Revolutionary Research into the Biology of Near-Death* (2000, Inner Traditions Bear and Company) However, his research was beset with the problems of regulation and eventually he had to give it up because the costs of obtaining the licences and of the DMT itself were crippling. Using DMT in research is however a challenge for a number of reasons other illegality and cost. For a start it can't be taken orally because it's broken down in the gut and liver very fast. That's because ayahuasca is a mixture of two plants, and one of them produces a substance (an enzyme inhibitor) that prevents the breakdown of the DMT from the other plant. Getting consistent preparations with the right amounts of the two plant products is difficult and unlikely to get through typical UK ethical approvals.

It would be possible to give a synthetic version of the plant enzyme inhibitor, such as the MAOI moclobemide, and then take pure DMT by mouth but then we get into the problem of safety. We can't be certain that this novel mixture of synthetic drugs would be safe, as its not been used before, so the regulators would demand many expensive safety studies before allowing us to use this combination. Another route is to use smoked DMT but again this presents problems of accurately assessing the dose someone would take in through the lungs. In the end we decided the only viable way was to give synthetic DMT intravenously, as Strassman had done, and with his guidance as to speed of administration and dosage to use.

However, this doesn't solve all the problems because DMT has a very short half-life in the body, i.e. its actions are limited to under ten minutes before it's broken down in the liver and blood. This presents a real challenge for imaging studies where we prefer to have effects that last up to an hour to maximise the quality of the imaging data we collect. So, Chris Timmermans a PhD student in our group worked out a compromise from building simulations of the time course of DMT in the blood following intravenous injections, using data provided by a Swedish clinical pharmacologist colleague, Professor Michael Ashton from Gothenburg. We developed a protocol whereby we give DMT by IV injections with a plan to do two injections in sequence, about 15 minutes apart so allowing about 30 mins of scanning time. During this pre-trial phase we also tested out the utility of EEG (brain wave) measures to reveal the impact of the drug because in our LSD and psilocybin studies we had found that brain waves measured by MEG were profoundly altered.

This approach turned out to be remarkably effective. We started with a low dose of DMT (7mg) and found it produced quite marked alterations in visual experiences. These were magnified at a higher (14mg) dose, and at the highest (20mg) dose tested profound alterations were found that were congruent with those reported by many people who have a successful ayahuasca experience. These include alterations in subjective state such as entering a different dimension, the loss of sense of self, spiritual feelings and a sense of one-ness with the universe. We were intrigued by the common experience that ayahuasca and DMT users have of seeing (or 'sensing') extra-terrestrial beings or 'entities' when they escape from current reality so we asked them to draw their visual experiences once the trip had ended. Several subjects who got the highest dose drew images of shapes resembling people or entities! The plan now is to repeat this procedure using as a standard dose of 18mg per person in an fMRI scanner to see if we can detect the location and origins of these creatures/experiences in the brain.

One particularly common experience of DMT users is that of being transported into another dimension where the entities live. Some describe it as if 'passing though a "wormhole" into hyperspace or through a door into another universe.' Others say it's entering into a higher dimension of consciousness where a powerful ambience of love exudes from the entities and even the space they are in. This new dimension or universe is felt as more real, more vivid and more meaningful than the current one.

One immediate output of the current study is that we have collaborated with the Coma Science Group in Liege, Belgium who research near death experiences. Because the enzymes to make DMT exist in the brain (especially the pineal gland) and because of seeming similarities between these two states of altered consciousness there has been a lot of discourse in the psychedelic field about the possible role of brain-produced DMT in the near death experience phenomenon. The idea that DMT produces near death experiences has been undermined by a detailed scientific analysis conducted by Professor Dave Nichols from Purdue. But there had never been a comparison of the two subjective states. So, Chris Timmermans plotted a graph of the scale of DMT experiences against those collected by the Belgian group from people who had recovered from near death experiences and who filled-out the same questionnaire. He found a considerable overlap in symptoms: the DMT participants score quite highly on the near-death experience scale, and in a range similar to those who had near death experiences. The near-death experience group had more religious and transcendental/out-of-body experiences but otherwise the scale of the subjective reports was largely the same.

Such powerful experiences explain why many DMT users seek to return to it on occasions to renew the experience and insights they gain; often they re-engage with the same entity who can support them and give them advice and wisdom. The funding for our DMT imaging study was provided by one such 'psychonaut' who wished to know if there might be a brain basis of his profound experiences. We shall soon learn if DMT is different from LSD and psilocybin in terms of brain imaging changes. I predict it will have similar brain actions to the other two though as this occurs even more rapidly than with the other psychedelics this may explain the sudden shift into another dimension of consciousness. Nonetheless the experiences are real and live on in powerful memories. They pose a challenge to modern neuroscience in terms of how and why they occur. They also offer an insight into other forms of altered consciousness such as delusion, delirium and dreaming. Some of the experiences reported under DMT and other psychedelics support Jungian concepts of archetypes and might offer a new way of developing research into the brain basis of psychoanalysis.

From brain imaging to future therapeutics

Finally I want to come back to the issue of using drugs to produce behavioural change for clinical benefit. Has our research on psychedelics opened a new door to therapy? In a word yes! George Goldsmith and Katja Malievskaia and their team have set up a company called COMPASS Pathways to develop psilocybin as a medicine for people with treatment-resistant depression. They have developed a reliable and regulatory-compliant source of synthetic psilocybin and have approval from the European Medicines Agency to conduct a multi-centre trial of a single 25mg psilocybin session (compared with a 1mg or a 10mg dose) with supportive psychotherapeutic integration as in our trial. This will be conducted in several countries simultaneously and if this is successful then approval in Europe might soon follow.

One major challenge with psychedelic research is that the effects of the 'active' treatment with psilocybin are so clear that participants would easily be able to work out whether they are on the active drug or a placebo. This makes the 'blind' weak, and so we wondered if there were control treatments we could use other than placebo. One option would be another drug with profound brain effects such as ketamine, but this also has anti-depressant actions, so would reduce the power of the study to find a difference. The John Hopkins group used the stimulant drug methylphenidate as this activates the brain, though in a different way to psychedelics, whereas the New York University group used a niacin placebo, that causes facial flushing. But methylphenidate is also a weak anti-depressant and flushing isn't very likely to be mistaken for psilocybin.

After a great deal of consideration we decided that in our new psilocybin depression study we would use a high (25mg) psilocybin dose as before and compare the effects with a low (1mg ineffective) dose of psilocybin. In this way everyone gets psilocybin and the same level of psychotherapy, so expectation effects are minimised. Also we have decided that those who get the low (ineffective) dose of psilocybin will then be treated for six weeks with escitalopram, the most efficacious SSRI; whereas those who got the high (effective) dose of psilocybin will be given six weeks of placebo tablets. Of course, all this will be done with both the patients and the researchers fully blinded. This approach will allow us to compare high dose psilocybin with the best SSRI in terms of clinical outcomes and adverse effects.

Microdosing — Less is more?

An alternative perspective is that of microdosing drugs such as psilocybin and LSD. Microdosing is a term used for administration of drugs at lower than usual doses. This means using doses too low to have overt psychedelic effects, so for example 10–20 micrograms of LSD or 0.5mg of psilocybin. These may have subtle acute subjective effects such as relaxation or mild social enhancement — similar to the effects when a small dose of ayahuasca is used in the Santo Daime church ceremonies we learn about in the next chapter. But the doses are too low to produce alterations in perception or consciousness. Dosing is typically taken two-to-three times a week though some people use daily. Over time it is thought that these mild effects may improve brain function, perhaps through increasing resilience to stress (as serotonin seems to do in general) or maybe the subtle stimulation of 5-HT2A receptors by microdosing a psychedelic can make the brain more flexible and creative. We know that commercial unpublished studies testing the safety of microdosing LSD have already been conducted in preparation for more extensive clinical trials, and though the results are not yet published we understand no serious adverse effects were found. Still we cannot be sure that taking these drugs even at low doses every day will not throw up unexpected adverse effects in the long-term. It would be helpful if some means were found to collect safety data from the thousands of people that say they are microdosing on a regular basis across the western world.

This approach has been encouraged by Dr James Fadiman, a longstanding psychedelic researcher, who began studying these drugs in the 1960s when they were legal. Recent media reports suggest that microdosing LSD is being taken up by those working in information and technology industries such as in Silicon Valley to improve their creativity and outputs. Microdosing with LSD for life-improvement was recently popularised in a best-selling book by the New York writer Ayelet Waldman, *A Really Good Day: How Microdosing*

Made a Mega Difference in My Mood, My Marriage, and My Life (2017, Knopf Publishing Group).

Others go further and suggest that microdosing of psychedelics might even protect against brain damage and dementia because they may have neurogenesis properties which might promote the growth of new neurons in the brain. Certainly the longevity of some of the earliest users of LSD such as Albert Hofmann and Joel Elkes, both of whom lived till over 100-years-of-age, suggests that premature deaths and claims of 'fried brains' are not an inevitable consequence of psychedelic use! One famous long-retired but still sprightly and active professor of psychiatry smiled when I shared this insight with him and commented that this explained why he was doing so well even in his 80s! Some experts believe that 5-HT2A agonist drugs can reduce inflammation and so might be useful in conditions such asthma and rheumatoid arthritis, and this effect can be mediated without any unwanted effects in the brain.

The psychedelic treatment revolution across the globe

We are not the only group to have pioneered the use of psilocybin for treatments of people with psychiatric problems like depression. Several US groups, in New York and John Hopkins universities have been conducting studies of therapeutic benefits of psilocybin, particularly when used in patients with life changing diagnoses such as cancer or untreatable neurological disorders. In Switzerland, Peter Gasser has conducted an LSD study in patients with terminal disorders and in 2016 two major controlled trials of psilocybin for end of life anxiety and depression in people with terminal or life-threatening diagnoses were simultaneously reported. Both used a very similar design with psilocybin assessed against active placebo and achieved very similar outcomes. Psilocybin was found to be more efficacious than placebo and to deliver a clearly valuable clinical outcome. The fact that two separate groups found the same outcomes is most reassuring as each study provides a form of replication for the other.

The other major target for psychedelic treatment is in the field of *addiction*. Arguably the most profound example of a psychedelic trip changing someone's whole life and then changing the world was that of Bill Wilson the founder of Alcoholics Anonymous (AA). During his last detox from alcohol he had a psychedelic experience that opened his mind to another way of thinking, one free from his alcohol addiction. From this insight Bill developed AA and also persuaded the National Institutes of Health (NIH) in the US to fund trials of psychedelic treatment with LSD for alcoholism. In the end six trials were performed and a recent meta-analysis by two Norwegian psychologists found just a couple of LSD treatments could produce more profound and enduring reductions of drinking than any treatment before or since.

I have estimated that since psychedelics were banned in the late-1960s over 100 million people worldwide have died prematurely from alcohol use. If only ten per cent had responded to psychedelic treatment that would have saved ten million deaths. But they have been denied this opportunity because of the politically driven desire to control psychedelic drug use, which the ban had virtually no impact on! Such mind changing effects of psychedelics on addiction have recently been resurrected by two research groups in the US. In Baltimore, the John Hopkins group have conducted a trial of psilocybin as a treatment for smoking cessation. They used their standard 25mg psilocybin dose plus supportive psychotherapy in a group of 15 smokers who were trying to quit. All but three were able to completely stop smoking for at least six months following this therapeutic intervention. This outcome is at least three times as powerful as the best current licensed treatment for smoking cessation which is the medicine varenicline—which works to reduce nicotine. Moreover, it required just three treatments over six months rather than repeated daily dosing. It appears that psilocybin works in a very different manner to varenicline in that it markedly increases positive outlook on life and enhances spiritual feelings.

Similarly, in New Mexico, Michael Bogenschutz and his team conducted a pilot study of psilocybin—this time for ten people with alcohol addiction who were trying to stop. They were given a dose of about 25mg on the first occasion which was four weeks into their standard treatment programme and a further dose of about 30mg four weeks later if they wanted it and were still in the trial (seven did). The main effect was seen after the first dose when a profound improvement of drinking behaviour was seen as a reduction in total days they drank and in the number of heavy drinking days. This benefit persisted for the rest of the trial with little impact of the second psilocybin dose but this is probably because the patients had improved so much there was little more for them to gain (a pattern known as a 'floor effect').

Ibogaine is becoming widely used in 'underground' treatment centres around the world for the treatment of heroin addiction and more recently methamphetamine addiction. It has recently been approved in Brazil but to date New Zealand is the one western country in the world where ibogaine is a licensed medicine. Addiction treatment groups in Dunedin and North Island have been using it in the treatment of heroin addiction for a number of years now. There is now a published report of their treatments which shows they have good outcomes with minimal adverse effects.

The major downside to ibogaine treatment is that it can have an effect on the heart rhythm that could lead to major complications, including cardiac arrest which probably accounts for the 37 deaths reported over the past few decades. The heart complication is particularly problematic because ibogaine is usually given during opioid withdrawal when the physiological strains on the heart are at their greatest. It might be possible to minimise these by using ibogaine after a successful standard detox though this would extend the time costs of a treatment package. Recent work from Paul Glue's team in Dunedin have shown that the impact of ibogaine on the heart is dose-related, so using lower doses with careful cardiac monitoring would seem to be a sensible way forward. There is also interest in some derivatives of ibogaine that are free of cardiac problems as potential new therapeutic agents. Also, we don't have imaging data on ibogaine so can't say if it's a typical psychedelic like psilocybin or not. We have in 2020 been awarded funding from the Alexander Mosley Charitable Trust for just this research and are now working out how to do such a study safely.

Perhaps not unexpectedly ayahuasca is also being developed as a treatment in South America with the first study providing evidence of efficacy in depression from a single psychedelic dose. This trial was conducted using a placebo-controlled design and the anti-depressant benefit of ayahuasca was found at one day after the treatment and lasted for at least a week. This is the first controlled study that gives scientific support to the body of personal accounts posted on the web of the value of a South American ayahuasca experience for lifting depression.

Might brain disorders other than depression and addiction also respond to psychedelic treatment? We shall soon find out as we are setting-up trials in anorexia and OCD to start in 2021. The John Hopkins group have nearly completed a controlled trial in cigarette dependence and anorexia. Dr James Rutter at King's College London, one of our clinicians in the first psilocybin-depression study has now set up his own research group and has been awarded an NHS grant to try to replicate our psilocybin efficacy study in patients with resistant depression. In Canada permission has been given for a few patients with terminal illness to be given psilocybin. And in the November 2020 US elections Oregon voted to make psilocybin treatment legal!

A major advance is that the regulators both in the US and Europe have acknowledged that psilocybin and MDMA are exciting innovations in medical treatment and have awarded each fast track status. This means that if the current Phase 2 trials are positive they will accelerate approvals and allow more detailed safety data to be collected in Phase 4 once they have been registered. Neurological conditions such as neuropathic pain and cluster headaches may also respond to psychedelics and we are planning a study in neuropathic pain.

So what links all these different disorders that might make them susceptible to psychedelic? I think this is (with the exception of cluster headaches) that all these disorders are internalising. The patient becomes over-engaged with internal thoughts. In depression this thinking is about their past failings, in addictions craving for alcohol or other drugs and in anorexia and OCD ruminations on weight and cleanliness, respectively. These thoughts are entrenched in the DMN and because psychedelics disrupt this network they might disrupt the thinking. This would allow patients to experience a temporary escape from their thinking and for some they may be able to hold that new way of thinking and stay free from their disorder for months or more.

If all, or just some, of these studies turn-out to be successful then we might, after 50 years of the censorship of psychedelics, regain the hope we had in the 1960s of heralding a revolution in medicine, of the same magnitude as happened for music and art.

CHAPTER 15

Moving MDMA back into the Clinic

Although studies with psilocybin have dominated the renaissance in psyche-delic research in the past decade work with other drugs is beginning and may soon also reach the clinical arena. After the censorship of research on psych-edelics, perhaps the greatest negative impact the UN conventions have had on research relates to that on MDMA, or 'ecstasy' as it is known more commonly. In *Chapter 5* I discussed the rise of MDMA — its potential for therapy and its banning because of the rave culture making it a Schedule 1 drug. As one might have predicted, this ban had little impact on recreational use of MDMA but immediately stopped its therapeutic use.

Despite continued cogent protests from US marital therapists, the ban has persisted and the use of MDMA as a medicine has been denied to the medical profession for over 30 years. Recently a new attempt to rehabilitate MDMA as a medicine has developed because of groundbreaking work where just two treatments with a dose of 125mg MDMA given in a therapeutic setting with concomitant psychotherapy has been shown to have remarkable efficacy in treatment-resistant post traumatic stress disorder (PTSD). This anxiety dis-order is one of the most prevalent and can be very difficult to treat. It is also the most rapidly growing psychiatric disorder in the world. Over 20 per cent of the Rwandan population is reported to suffer from PTSD following the genocide and it would seem likely that at least half of all Syrians have been similarly traumatised. The same is true in the military which has significantly higher levels of suicide. Remarkably it seems now that more US service per-sonnel have killed themselves than have been killed by enemy action in Iraq and Afghanistan, and many of these suffered from PTSD.

The effectiveness of MDMA as a treatment for marital breakdown of trust and affection, plus the growing evidence of efficacy in PTSD, raises questions about its mechanism of action. We know that MDMA causes the release of serotonin in the brain, but it has very different subjective effects from other serotonin enhancing drugs such as the psychedelics and the SSRIs. This seems to be because MDMA directly releases serotonin rather than mimics some of its action like the psychedelics do, or block re-uptake like the SSRIs do. However, the brain actions of MDMA in humans have hardly been studied because of its illegal status.

In addition MDMA can stimulate the release of oxytocin. This is a natural hormone that is critical in pregnancy as it facilitates the let-down of milk and enhances mother-baby bonding. In adults the role of oxytocin is less clear, but it may be part of the biological processes that make couples feel warmer towards each other after making love. Experiments from Harriet de Wit's team in Chicago have shown that MDMA can improve empathy and reduce activity in the fear centres of the brain particularly the amygdala.

Given the significant body of evidence of its therapeutic potential, and because about half million young people in the UK use MDMA each week, I had wanted to explore its actions in the brain for some time—but couldn't get funding. A couple of years ago I was approached by Channel 4 who were interested in doing some groundbreaking drugs experiments on live television. They asked me to do a science programme in which participants would be studied when using cocaine live on camera. I refused on the grounds that this could simply be construed as sensationalism—and besides research groups in the US had already used neuroimaging to show what cocaine does in the brain.

Channel 4 went away rather disappointed but a few weeks later returned to enquire if there was any Class A illegal drug I would be prepared to research on live television. I responded at once—'Yes, MDMA'–for the reasons given above. The subsequent programme was remarkable for many reasons. Not only was it the most detailed analysis of the brain actions of MDMA ever performed but also almost certainly the first serious scientific study ever funded by a television company. It was also at the time the most downloaded programme ever in the history of Channel 4, which for a scientific documentary was exceptional.

The results were as startling as the funding source. We discovered that, as with psilocybin, the effect of MDMA was only to decrease brain activity, but in quite different regions from those affected by the psilocybin. This finding proves that MDMA is not a psychedelic, which helps undermine the principle in the

US legislation against MDMA which is founded on the presumption that it is both a psychedelic and stimulant (and so the US gives MDMA users and dealers double the sentence they would get from either class of drug alone) (ACLU, 2012). The key effects of MDMA were to reduce activity in brain regions such as the amygdala and hippocampus that are intimately involved in re-living stress. Also, under MDMA the emotional content of negative memories was attenuated, which may explain why it can help people recover from PTSD.

Because we were interested in the possible effects of MDMA on memory, we had to collect some important recollections from each participant. So, before the scanning we got the participants to write down six of their best memories and six of their worst. As we didn't want to influence them we asked them to keep these to themselves but to remember each and then give it a simple name (e.g. honeymoon in Paris = good; was told my friend is dead = bad). We were then provided with these tags so that in the scanner we could ask them to recall each memory at a specific time. They were asked to recall three good and three bad memories during the *placebo* scan; and the other three good ones along with three bad memories during the MDMA scan. Each memory had to be held in their mind for 20 seconds. Afterwards they were asked to score the vividness and emotional strength of each memory on a 0–100 scale.

We found, as we had predicted, that under MDMA the positive memories were more positive and more vivid. However, the bad memories were scored as equally vivid and intense under MDMA as under placebo, but the negative valence of the bad memories was reduced by the MDMA. These brain actions are what we would want in a drug for the treatment for PTSD. A reduction in the valence of the traumatic memory would allow patients to cope better with the psychotherapeutic process that involves reliving the trauma in the care of the therapist and so gaining cognitive control over the emotions the memory reactivates.

The key effects of MDMA were to reduce activity in brain regions such as the amygdala and hippocampus that are intimately involved in the re-living of stress. Also, under MDMA the emotional content of negative memories was attenuated, which I think may explain why it can help people recover from PTSD.

Remarkably and quite unexpectedly one of our subjects, who had not previously disclosed she had been traumatised, said after the MDMA session:

'An interesting thing occurred in the MRI when I reached back for the bad memories, they did not seem bad. In fact they seemed to have been fatalistic necessities for the occurrence of the later good events I had to recall.'

She told us afterwards that the process of bad memory recall under MDMA was helpful to her recovery from the prior trauma. The power of this MDMA effect was such that it worked even though the drug was given as part of an experimental study designed to look at brain function rather than as part of a treatment.

MDMA has a number of pharmacological features that make it a potentially powerful augmentation treatment for PTSD. It increases empathy and so builds trust between therapist and patient. Also, it reduces anxiety so that the patient can re-engage with the memory of the trauma without losing control. This is critical because, as shown by the work of Professor Edna Foa at the University of Pennsylvania, the critical element in being fully recovered from PTSD is that the patient can talk about the trauma without experiencing the fear and other emotional reactions that were present at the time and which initially overwhelmed them.

It is impossible ever to forget the factual reality of the trauma. What distinguishes people who suffer from PTSD from those who have experienced similar traumas but do not have the disorder is that the PTSD sufferers cannot suppress the emotional components when they engage factual memories. This means they are perpetually re-experiencing the fear, or living with the fear, of suddenly re-experiencing it (either of which can be equally stressful).

In addition to several landmark papers on its actions on the brain, there was another important output of our MDMA study — the dose we used was safe. We chose to use 100mg of the hydrochloride salt as this is equivalent to 80mg pure MDMA base or two typical 40mg ecstasy tablets. We found this MDMA dose was well tolerated by our subjects despite the unusual location of being in an MRI brain scanner. Only one person had a bad reaction, and this was due to them not declaring at the screening interview that they suffered from claustrophobia. Many people find being in an MRI scanner quite unpleasant as it's a long narrow tube that you can feel trapped in. Claustrophobia is therefore a contra-indication for undertaking an fMRI scan and he should have told us before agreeing to the study.

This person's reaction turned out to be of interest as he was the only one in whom the MDMA session produced more activity in the amygdala than was seen in the placebo session. We know that anxiety increases activity in the amygdala so this response was exactly as one would predict from the fact that this volunteer was more anxious during that scan. This finding provides an indirect but valuable internal control for the validity of our findings; anxiety reduction under MDMA is associated with (and likely due to) a decrease in amygdala activity. Similar findings have also been reported by the one US group that has overcome the barriers to studying this drug. This is that of Harriett de Wit at the University of Chicago, who found that the typical fear response of enhanced amygdala activation was attenuated when people were exposed to fear-producing visual images under MDMA compared with that under placebo.

As well as showing that this MDMA dose was safe to administer without negative effects in the brain or body we also found no obvious negative effects in the medium or longer-term afterwards. A phenomenon commonly called 'the Monday blues' is often reported after a heavy weekend session of MDMA use. Some people think it may be due to depletion of serotonin produced by MDMA. The fact we did not find any evidence for such a carry-over effect in our study suggests that it is not simply due to MDMA use alone. More likely it is a consequence of the other activities that users engage in such a dancing all night as well as taking other drugs, particularly alcohol or ketamine. It is possible that MDMA might make the brain more vulnerable to the effects of exhaustion, sleep deprivation and other drug use, but this would need a specific systematic study.

What is now needed is cutting-edge research on the effects of MDMA when used in the treatment of PTSD. The American organization the Multidisciplinary Association for Psychedelic Studies (MAPS) has been pioneering international studies of MDMA psychotherapy for PTSD, setting them up in Switzerland, Canada and Israel as well as in the US. The MDMA research field received a great boost in August 2017 when MAPS received the good news that the Federal Drugs Administration (FDA) had given them fast track 'breakthrough therapy' approval for their development of MDMA as a treatment for PTSD in the US. This means that they just need to prove efficacy in a single multi-centre-controlled trial to gain a licence for MDMA to become a medicine.

We are in the process of working with MAPS (who are supplying the MDMA medicine) and the Alexander Mosley Charitable Trust to explore if their two-session MDMA treatment model might help PTSD-suffering alcoholics who drink to deaden their traumatic memories. It is possible that, if they overcome their PTSD syndrome, they may then be able to reduce their drinking. This study is being led by Dr Ben Sessa in my group and has been challenging but rewarding. So far, all the 14 patients entered into the study have successfully completed the 12 week treatment course and all stayed abstinent throughout it, and beyond. At the nine month end point only a third had returned to drinking. This is in a marked contrast to the outcomes of our current NHS-standard treatment course where we find that only a quarter stay abstinent for this long. Such remarkable outcomes are rare in the treatment of alcoholism and I hope our results will provoke further trials or even lead to MDMA therapy being given compassionate use status as is possible in Switzerland.

We have also explored in another study with Professor Mitul Mehta from King's College London the effects on MDMA (and psilocybin) on interpersonal interactions. To do this we used a well-established method of assessing empathy for others — The Ultimatum Game. One player, the proposer, is given a sum of money and asked to split it with the other player, the responder. The responder decides whether to accept or reject the offered split. If the offer is accepted, the money is divided as offered. If the offer is rejected, neither player receives any money at all. While the 'rational' decision is for the responder to accept any amount of money offered in a one-off interaction, studies typically find that the majority of people reject low, unequal offers. Previous work using SSRIs has shown increasing brain serotonin with the chronic use of these drugs will reduce the rejection rate for unfair offers — serotonin makes people more accommodating of injustice. In contrast, depleting serotonin using the technique of tryptophan depletion had the opposite effect. We found that MDMA (and in another experiment — psilocybin) had an effect like the SSRIs — it made people more likely to accept less fair offers. This supports the developing idea that increasing serotonin makes people more pro-social and supportive — or at least accepting — of others' attitudes.

The studies of MDMA in PTSD and our evidence that it acts on key emotional centres to reduce fear memories means there is now a strong rationale for future work. A study to explore the effects of MDMA on brain processes in

PTSD using fMRI brain imaging is planned in collaboration with the PTSD expert centre in Cardiff University with Professor Jon Bisson. This work is funded by the Beckley Foundation and MAPS and has taken longer to initiate than hoped due to insurance and regulatory issues in the local hospital trusts.

Dr Ben Sessa in our team has just completed the first trial of MDMA plus psychotherapy in the treatment of alcoholism. He found that just two doses (as used in the PTSD studies) had a profound impact in helping people stay abstinent after the treatment course had ended. These results are being written up and the full paper is expected to be published in 2021 — so watch this space!

CHAPTER 16

Coda: Further Reflections and Timeline

I was born on the 16 April 1951 at Southmead Hospital Bristol to (Reginald) John Nutt and Eileen May Baber. I was the first of their three children, all boys. My dad, Jack (as John always called himself) was a tall elegant gentle man forced to live his life in the shadow of what might had been, as aged 16 he had to leave grammar school early. His younger brother Norman had caught polio that gave him leg paralysis, so dad had to earn money working in the local Co-op store to pay for the medical treatment in those pre-NHS days. Leaving school early scuppered Dad's university ambitions and it was left to me to be the first person in our family to achieve this milestone. The damaging consequences of such health care inequalities before the establishment of the NHS has been a major reason for my strong commitment to the NHS concept of free health care for all throughout the whole of my life.

The experience of payment-only medical care made my father a lifelong convinced socialist and trade unionist. True to his beliefs he refused to buy a home, insisting property ownership was in effect stealing land, so we lived in a council house on one of the most notorious estates in Bristol—Hartcliffe. There were a couple of other idiosyncratic features of the Nutt household that probably contributed to my academic success. One was we never had a TV—so we read books in the evenings. We also had discussions over meals. And since there was me and my two brothers plus my dad, these discussions often ended in a row over politics or sport. The second reason was we didn't have phone. To accept my place at Cambridge I had to go to the local phone box several streets away—luckily that evening it wasn't vandalised!

Dad worked as a civil servant in HM Customs & Excise almost all his life and the high point came when he was able to join the working team that Harold Wilson set-up to develop a Green Paper on the nationalising of land and property, so fulfilling his dream of common ownership. Sadly the project didn't come to fruition so he so spent the rest of his life focusing on his golf (he was of course an artisan (reduced fee and rights) not a member (a different class) until the former were abolished, his family, especially his grandchildren, and solving the *Times* crossword each day (he would almost always better my efforts).

My mother Eileen was a bundle of nervous energy. I am often asked where I get my energy from and I always reply, 'My mother.' She was a relentlessly dedicated one who continued her drive and love when she became a grandmother. Her memory of total positive regard and support for my own children I still revere today. I was fortunate to inherit her drive and motivation alongside (or so I hope) my father's high intelligence.

My childhood seemed idyllic at the time. We always lived on the outskirts of town, because that's where the 1950s council estates were placed, so there were plenty of fields and woods to play in. Apparently, I was a competitive and aggressive child and my mum recounts occasions when other mothers would come to our door complaining I had hurt or upset their child. My brothers Bryan (two years younger) and Norman ('Sam,' four years younger) also suffered my unpleasant side. My bullying nature came to an abrupt end when I was about seven. The family had by then moved to Chatham in Kent from where my father commuted daily by train to the main Customs House in the City of London. In Kent I was an obvious outsider with a very different accent and so was picked on by the local kids. One summer day in the local fields I was beaten-up by three local lads who I had assumed were my friends because we went to the same school. I came home to my mother in tears and she was her usual caring self. I remember her getting me to reflect on the nature of bullying and promising myself and her I would never do it again. And I never have. In fact, opposing bullying and injustice in all forms has since become a life theme.

I was always a somewhat paradoxical child. Outgoing, seemingly confident and chatty, yet inside very anxious. My first memory is when about two-years-of-age my mother went shopping and left me behind with my grandmother Nanny Nutt. I stood on the steps of the end of terrace Victorian house wailing as my mum disappeared down the road. Separation anxiety figured a lot in my first decade which may explain why such a lot of my research has been on anxiety disorders. I always was anxious being away from my family, so much so that unlike my more relaxed brothers I was too anxious to sleep away from home. I didn't manage that goal till I was eleven-years-old. It was this anxiety that led the family to move from Bristol to Kent. My dad had been promoted and posted to London just after I had started infants school. He decided to commute each week from Sunday evening till Friday, leaving us behind in Bristol where the two parental families could help my mum out (three children under five was a heavy burden for a solo parent). After a few weeks of his weekly absences I am told my behaviour at school began to change. The teachers were concerned I was more irritable, anxious and aggressive. Though I can't recall it, apparently I was seen by a psychologist and told them that I really missed my dad. They recommended we moved to be nearer London so we could stay together as a family. And so we did—we moved to Chatham when I was six.

I don't have any recollection of problems at school but vividly remember one Sunday afternoon when I had been out playing on the green and came in for tea, only to discover my dad was just leaving to get the train to London. I burst into tears and was inconsolable for hours. It must have hurt him too and it emphasised the need to relocate us for a more regular family life. Moving from a council house to another nearer London wasn't easy. A swop had to be done and often this involved a chain of swops, in those days before the internet it was all done by newspapers that listed council house tenants looking to move and correspondence was by letter. Like many of our neighbours we didn't have a home phone till the 1970s.

My first school day in Bristol was another example of my anxiety. My mum had to drag me protesting to the gates where I was sucked into the large crowd of five-year-olds. I was so anxious about drawing attention to myself (we would now call this 'social anxiety') that I didn't dare raise my hand to ask to be allowed to go to the loo, so wet myself. On the other hand, I loved the content of school. Lots and lots of learning—reading and writing and books everywhere. And there was also music. At that time, the BBC schools network broadcast musical lessons. Each week we were taken into the hall and allowed to develop our own expressive dances to the music of the day. My abiding memory is Grieg's 'In the Hall of the Mountain King.' This is so evocative of trolls and other nocturnal creatures and I remember stomping around the hall pretending I was one of these.

The other great pleasure of school was talking with the other children. Getting to explore ideas and controversies. Was there a God? If not, how did we get here? But then if there was a God who created him? Simple questions I thought but neither the other kids nor the teachers could answer them. And of course, still today no-one can.

The impact of school on me was profound. That first afternoon I returned home completely converted, never again was I anxious about going to school, at least not until I came across my first sadistic teacher. This occurred a few years later in my second year of junior school — so I was eight. For the first time I had a male teacher and this came as quite a shock. The year before we had been in Miss Taylor's class: a beautiful, warm, caring and nurturing person who you wanted to see every day. I was in love for the first time! But the new man was completely different. It may have been his first class ever, I am not sure, but his approach was the opposite of Miss Taylor's. He was aggressive and threatening and worst of all violent. He would throw books at you and sometimes the board eraser (which had a wooden back so hurt).

Worse he liked to use a ruler on the back of the hand to punish poor performance and wielded it on a daily basis. Being one of the smarter ones in the class I rarely performed sufficiently badly to be beaten, and was just the recipient of the thrown books. One of which missed me and went out of the window and when I pointed this out to 'Sir' he replied, 'That's the best place for rubbish like that.' The worst punishment was reserved for Tom, the least intellectually able boy in the class — now we would probably diagnose him as dyslexic. He kept getting his maths tables wrong and was beaten almost every day for this. I was scared, anxious and nauseated by this teacher's sadism. That was the only year of my whole school career I didn't enjoy. The contrast with my next male teacher, Mr Gregory (whom we met back in *Chapter 1*) when I was at Teyfant Junior Mixed School in Bristol was profound. Rather than scaring me he inspired me into learning and science.

We were together for four years as a nuclear family in Kent but the extended family was all in Bristol and after a few years my mum wanted to move back nearer to them. Dad gave up the idea of career progression in London and got his old job back in the Bristol Customs House — refurbished after being burnt down in the 1831 riots — and his career then plateaued. Bristol was good for me as I passed my eleven plus exam and went to the top grammar school there, Bristol Grammar School (BGS).

The eleven plus has been a topic of continual debate since before I took it and to the present day. My class was a microcosm of the issues. Of the 40 pupils in my junior school (the top two classes in that year) seven passed the exam. But I was the only one who chose to use this success to go to grammar school. The other six decided to stay with their friends and attend the local secondary modern school. Academic ambition wasn't something they or their families cared about. But for me it was important to fulfil my potential and get the university education my father had desired but been denied. I often wonder whether the other six regretted not grabbing this opportunity of a more empowering education.

In September 1961, I set off for my first day at senior school — holding my father's hand for the last time as a child because I was scared of the challenge ahead. BGS was a boys only direct grant school, so half the pupils were eleven plus boys and half fee paying. The latter had largely come up through prep school which was on the same campus so were much more *au fait* with the ethos and attitudes of the senior school. The eleven plussers were rather more plebeian and so we were put together in two classes called 'shells.' I later learnt that this referred to small shell-shaped recesses in the old great hall where these 'outsiders' used to be taught. A year later we were fused with the paying lot based on exam results which determined our status and class level. The top classes were then fast tracked to O-levels in three years — a ploy to give those academically-inclined ones in the top classes an extra year at school after A-levels to prepare for the Oxbridge entry exams. This was the expectation and it worked for me. I assumed I would go either to Oxford or Cambridge. The question was what to study there?

In the end I decided — or rather was persuaded by the head of science at BGS — to go to Cambridge to study Natural Sciences. So, I applied — took the exams and to my amazement was awarded a prestigious open scholarship. The rest of this part of my life is in *Chapter 1*.

1972–1975 Guy's Hospital

These three years were some of the most inspiring of my life. It turned out I really enjoyed medicine and (so I believe) was quite good at it. Why did I chose Guy's? In the 1970s there were about ten London teaching hospitals that Oxbridge medics went to for their clinical training. At that time neither Oxford or Cambridge had good-enough or big-enough local hospitals to accommodate the 200 plus new students a year but London did. Students chose on the basis of location, expertise and sometimes paternal precedence—i.e. following in father's footsteps. The socially-minded students who were planning to become a GP went to the (now Royal) London Hospital with its socialist medicine ethos. The ones planning a career in private practice went to St Thomas' as it was near to the Houses of Parliament.

As I wanted to be an academic it was suggested that the Middlesex Hospital would be best as it had a good research reputation. But, once I looked around, I was unimpressed, not by the people but by the building. It was a great brick monstrosity (now demolished) without a single place to sit out in the sun. My girlfriend at the time, Jude, was at Guy's doing dentistry and suggested I looked there. I did and loved the fact that there was a park in the middle of the hospital—trees, flowers and grass. I applied and on the afternoon of my interview I sprawled out on the grass, with my shirt off, using the sun to stimulate my hypothalamus and reading Thomas De Quincey's *Confessions of an English Opium-Eater*. Luckily I knew just enough not to mention that at the interview and they let me in.

The very first morning set the scene. Five junior students with clean shirts and our best neckties waiting for the senior consultant Dr Hardwick. A man with a fearsome reputation as a clinician and 40-years of experience, his first words stuck with me for ever, and have underpinned my whole clinical practice.

'What is the purpose of medicine?' he asked us.

'Ummm,' we thought.

'To cure disease?' someone spluttered.

'No,' he replied.

'To save lives?'

'No.'

'To make a diagnosis?'

'No!' Then he explained: 'The purpose of medicine is to reduce suffering.'

That was the right answer. It's as true now as it was then though in this age of evidence-based medicine this seems often to be forgotten. Some doctors seem to treat patients as units in a statistical trial rather than as humans who are suffering and need support. When I hear a colleague say, 'There is no evidence to help this patient so I can discharge them,' I get quite upset. Often, I curtly suggest that they might try to develop some evidence, and in the meantime do what they can to reduce the suffering of the patient and their family.

I loved the challenge of making a diagnosis, which in those pre-imaging days (no MRIs then) was a real skill. Luckily for me I was a student at the start of the modern phase of medicine where the science underpinning many disorders began to be understood and to lead to new treatments. For example, I recall the introduction of the first histamine H2 antagonists for the treatment of peptic ulcers. These were some of the first designer drugs, i.e. molecules developed from an understanding of science, in medicine. Their discovery was later rewarded with the Nobel Prize to Professor James Black.

The idea that physiology could direct pharmacology and so therapeutics was thrilling and I began to wonder if it could be applied to my organ of interest—the brain. In reality, this has been the underpinning principle of my research ever since. During my training I was always known as a future psychiatrist, not least because when my year group were all off around the world for their elective period I stayed behind in London. I worked as a student and then locum doctor at the local community psychiatric hospital, St Olave's, a converted Victorian workhouse. Since the elective period came up before I had done any psychiatry it was in at the deep end. It was sink or swim. This meant working all day on the wards and then all night reading psychiatry textbooks!

In *Chapter 1* I tell the tale of the first patient I was asked to formally interview by myself, the man with 'smell hallucinations.' This patient raised two questions in my mind. What was going on his brain to make the fish smell? And why did the Stelazine help it to go away? No-one seemed to know the answer. Even today it's not clear why some people have hallucinations. But while I was at Guy's there was a major breakthrough in how antipsychotic drugs worked. In 1974 the dopamine receptor was discovered and drugs like Stelazine were shown to block it. Once I learned this, I became hooked on a career in psychopharmacology. If a simple molecule such as dopamine could alter the whole content of a person's thinking maybe the brain was explicable in chemical terms. Forty years on I still think there is traction in this concept.

Guy's Hospital also had another major impact on my life—because that's where I found my future partner and wife—Di, at the time a student nurse and later a ward sister and health visitor. We worked together on a couple of wards without real contact but then she turned up in our minor operations clinic to have a mole removed from her cheek. I had very steady hands so offered to take on the challenge. The mole was removed, sutures carefully applied and a few days later even the incision had disappeared. She was so pleased she invited me out for a meal to thank me and over 40 years later we are still together. We were married in 1979 and as well as being the brilliant mother of our four beautiful children, enthusiastic Labrador owner (ten so far) and cats (six so far), Di is my strongest and most loyal supporter and advocate. She's a great cook and is an ideal guest in an audience as she gets my jokes and has a loud laugh that encourages the others to join in!

Before specialising in psychiatry, I wanted to get a deeper understanding of the brain so began to apply for training jobs in neurology. I assumed that because I was one of their star students (I had won quite a few of the undergraduate medical prizes) that Guy's would welcome me, but I was wrong. My reputation for being a 'shrink' (slang for psychiatrist) in training was seen as a fatal flaw in my character, so the Guy's neurologists rejected me. Luckily, another major London teaching hospital—St Mary's—didn't know of my past affiliation with psychiatry. And despite nearly fatally messing-up my interview (more of which soon) I had the pleasure of spending six months training in neurology there under the tutelage of Dr Charles Edwards and Sir Roger Bannister (of four minute mile fame).

It turned out to be a very significant move for me because St Mary's research was led by Sir Stan Peart, a brilliant clinical pharmacologist, who had trained Professor David Grahame-Smith. He was now the director of the MRC Clinical Pharmacology Unit in Oxford, and it was this link that got me into my first research position in Oxford. This came after I had completed my higher exams in medicine to become a member of the Royal College of Physicians and fulfilled one of my travel ambitions, going to Australia via India, Burma and then to Malaysia and Bali.

The rest of my career story you have (presumably) already figured out from earlier chapters of this book. But I can't leave you wondering how I nearly messed up my St Mary's interview. In many ways my whole career trajectory pivoted on that placement as it got me into research at Oxford. So, what did I do wrong? Well at the time I had no idea I had done anything wrong, it wasn't until my leaving party six months later that I learned of my mistake. At the party, which I held in the hospital, I bumped into a female doctor and asked her who she was. She told me she was a registrar in the Sexual Disorders Clinic. Then she asked who I was? I said, 'It's my party' to which she replied, 'Ah — you're the David Nutt my consultant told me about — what not to say in an interview.' Despite its high alcohol content my blood froze! She then explained that when I had been asked if there were any other doctors in my family? (a question they wouldn't be allowed to ask today), 'No,' I had replied, 'I am the black sheep.' OK, not a great joke but it turned out the committee wanted to reject me because of this and despite my being the strongest candidate. I remember it clearly, thinking at the time I said it that the lack of laughter around the boardroom meant it hadn't gone down well. But I had never expected that this could have been a fatal mistake debarring me from the post. It turned out her consultant had argued my corner and persuaded them that I had proven clinical attributes and research potential that offset my poor sense of humour. I can't remember his name but am still very grateful for his intervention. And from that moment on I never joked in interviews again!

For the Record — Times and Dates

1969	Technician, Dr A Rogers, Physiology Department, Bristol University
1975	House Physician, Guy's Hospital
1976	House Surgeon, Royal Sussex County Hospital, Brighton
1976	Senior House Officer, Dermatology, Guy's Hospital
1977	Senior House Officer, Neurology, St Mary's Hospital, Paddington
1978	Senior House Officer, Psychiatry, Guy's Hospital
1978–1982	Clinical Scientist in the MRC Unit of Clinical Pharmacology, Radcliffe Infirmary, Oxford (Professor D G Grahame Smith)
1982–1983	Registrar in Psychiatry on the Oxford Rotational Training Scheme
1983–1985	Lecturer in Psychiatry, University of Oxford, attached to the Psychopharmacology Research Unit, Littlemore Hospital, Oxford
1985–1986	Wellcome Senior Fellow in Clinical Science, University Department of Psychiatry, Warneford Hospital, Oxford. Honorary Consultant Psychiatrist
1986–1988	Fogarty Visiting Scientist National Institutes of Health and Chief of the Section of Clinical Science, National Institute on Alcohol Abuse and Alcoholism, Bethesda, Maryland
1988–date	Director, Psychopharmacology Unit, University of Bristol; Senior Research Fellow in Pharmacology and in Mental Health; Honorary Consultant Psychiatrist, United Bristol Healthcare Trust
1994	Professor of Psychopharmacology, University of Bristol
1996–1997	Head, Division of Psychiatry, University of Bristol
1997–2003	Head of Department of Clinical Medicine
2000–2003	Dean of Clinical Medicine and Dentistry
2003–2008	Head of the Department of Community Based Medicine
2008–2016	Edmond J Safra Chair of Neuropsychopharmacology, Imperial College, London

2009	Founded Drug Science — originally called Independent Scientific Committee on Drugs (ISCD)

Awards and prizes

1972	Saunders Open Scholarship
1969–1975	Christchurch and Bushmills Scholarships
1972	Badminton 'Blue' Cambridge University
1972	Junior Common Room President, Downing College, Cambridge
1972–1975	Clinical Prizes: First Clinical Prize
	Gillespie Prize in Psychiatry
	Gilbert Prize in Rheumatology
	Dermatology Prize
	Beany Prize in Pathology
1972–1975	University 'Purple' and Captain of Badminton, London University
1975	Mental Health Trust Essay Competition: 'The Significance of Life Changes in the Development of Illness'
1984	Royal College of Psychiatrists Research Prize, Proxime Accessit: 'The Experimental Pharmacology of Anxiety: New Concepts of Benzodiazepine Receptor Function'
2009	*Daily Telegraph* Briton of the Year — Top 25
2009	Second (to Banksy) as Bristolian of the year
2010	Place 69 in the *Times* list of 100 most influential figures in UK science
2013	Winner of the John Maddox Prize for Standing up for Science
2014	The Transmission Prize for Science Communication

College appointments

1983–1988	Research Fellow in Medical Sciences, Corpus Christi College, Oxford

Learned societies — by examination or election

Royal College of Physicians (RCP)

Royal College of Psychiatrists (RCPsych)

British Association for Psychopharmacology (BAP) — Past President — 2000–2002

European College of Neuro-Psychopharmacology (ECNP) — President 2007–2010

Collegium Internationale Neuro-Psychopharmacologicum (CINP)

British Pharmacological Society (BPS)

Editor

1989–date	*Journal of Psychopharmacology*
2013–date	*Drug Science, Policy and Law*

University of Bristol

1989–1993	Member of the Scientific Committee of the Molecular Recognition Centre
2007	Director, Bristol Neuroscience

Other University Preferments

2004–date	Visiting Professor, University of Maastricht
2006–2011	Visiting Professor, Imperial College, University of London
2004–date	Visiting Professor, University of Otago, New Zealand
2006	Raine Visiting Professor, University of Western Australia

2014–date	Visiting Professor, The Open University

Royal College of Psychiatry

1990–1995	Basic Sciences Exam Committee (Part II)
1994–1997	Psychopharmacology Sub-Committee
1996–2000	Steering group of Biological Psychiatry Special Interest Group

Medical Research Council

1991	Subcommittee for Site Visit — Institute of Psychiatry
1992–1993	Neuroscience Approach to Mental Health steering group
1992–94	Addiction Field Review working party
1993–1997	Neuroscience Project Grant Committee
1994	Alcohol Treatment Research Working Group
1994	Suicide and Parasuicide Review Panel
1998–2005	Neuroscience Advisory Board
2006–2009	Neuroscience and Mental Health Board
2009–2012	Lead (with Robbins Cambridge) MRC ICCAM research cluster in Addiction
2009–2012	Addiction Initiative Stakeholder group

European Scientific Research Council

2010	UK Psychology Benchmarking Review Steering Group Member

UK Research Excellence Framework Assessment

2013–2014	Neuroscience Psychiatry and Psychology Panel Member

Government Responsibilities — Home Office

1996–2008	Advisory Council on the Misuse of Drugs (ACMD)
2008–2009	Chair of ACMD
2000–2008	Chair of Technical Committee, ACMD
2008	Cross Departmental Research Group
2008	Home Office Scientific Advisory Committee

Science and Technology/DTI/OSI

1995–1999	Parliamentary Office of Science and Technology 'Soft' Drugs Steering Committee
2003–2005	Scientific Lead DTI Foresight Programme 'Brain Science Addiction and Drugs'

Department of Health

1995–2000	Advisory Committee on NHS Drugs
2000–date	British National Formulary (BNF). Advisor on psychiatric medicines
2000–2005	Committee on Safety of Medicines
1999–date	NICE reviewer for depression, panic and social anxiety disorders and the Z-drug hypnotics

Ministry of Defence

1990–2004	Consultant
2005–2007	Member Defence Sciences Advisory Council (DSAC)

Parliamentary Evidence

2000	House of Lords Committee on Cannabis
2004	Home Affairs Committee on Drugs
2005	Evidence to All Party Drugs Interest Group
2006	Evidence to Select Committee on Science and Technology; Scientific Advice, Risk and Evidence:
2009	Cocaine and related drugs
2012	Home Affairs Select Committee Review of the Drug Laws

Miscellaneous

1997–2000	Drugs and the Law: Report of the Independent Inquiry into the Misuse of Drugs Act 1971 (Runciman Report) (Police Foundation, 2000). Member of the inquiry.
1993–2000	UBHT Medicines Advisory Committee
1993–1997	UBHT Medical Research Committee
1993–2000	District Psychiatric Training Committee
1994–1997	External Examiner, University of Birmingham
1996–date	British Pharmacological Society, Clinical Pharmacology Section Expert
2000–2001	British Association of Psychopharmacology — President
1998–2004	Trustee of the Sir Robert Mond Memorial Trust
1999–2001	BBSRC Functional Imaging Course Board Member
2011–2013	British Neuroscience Association President

International Positions

1993–1995	Faculty Member, European Certificate in Anxiety Disorder
1995–date	Director of the European Certificate of Affective Disorders Course
1996–1998	CINP International Scientific Program Committee member
1998–2017	ECNP Council Member
2007–2010	ECNP President
1999–2001	World Psychiatric Association, Co-Chair Section on Biological Psychiatry
1992	Member of the EC Working Party on PET and SPECT Ligands
2007–2011	Council Member European Brain Council
2011–2013	Vice President European Brain Council
2013–2017	President — European Brain Council
2010	Advisor Grand Challenges in Mental Health
2011–2012	Advisor to Swedish Government Review on Drug Alcohol and Tobacco Research
2012–2013	EU Scientific Committee for Month of the Brain 2013

Charitable work

2010–on	Founder and current Chair Drug Science (formerly ISCD)
2009–2014	Founder/Chair London Joint Working Group on Drug Abuse and Hepatitis C

Referee for grants and fellowships

MRC, BBSRC, ESRC, Wellcome Trust, The Netherlands MRC, NIHR, INSERM, German-Israeli research fund, NIH

Supervision of research students

Date completed	Student
1984	S Taylor DPhil (Oxon, with Dr Little)
1989	C Gleiter PhD (Tubigen)
1989	T Wolinski PhD (New York University)
1991	A McDermott PhD (London, CASE with Dr Wilkin)
1992	P Glue MD (Bristol)
1992	C Watson PhD (Nottingham, CASE with Dr Bennett)
1993	N French PhD (Strathclyde, CASE with Dr Pratt)
1993	S Jordan PhD (Aston, CASE with Dr Hanley)
1994	A Hudson PhD (Bristol)
1994	A Weinstein PhD (Bristol)
1997	L Lione PhD (CASE, with SmithKline Beecham)
1998	N Coupland MD (Bristol)
1998	A Malizia (MD)
1999	S Wilson PhD (Bristol)
1999	M Lalies PhD (Bristol)
1999	H Crofts PhD (with Dr Sue Wilson)
1999	C Parker PhD (with Dr Alan Hudson)
1999	C Bryce PhD (with Professor Smith, Psychology)
1999	E Robinson PhD (with Dr Alan Hudson)
2000	D Finn PhD (Bristol) (with Dr Alan Hudson)
2000	J Potokar MD (Bristol)
2002	R Price PhD (Bristol) (with Dr Alan Hudson)

2002	T Wright PhD (with Professor Smith, Psychology)
2003	C Bell MD (Bristol)
2003	N Muggleton PhD (with Dr Sue Wilson)
2003	M Edwards PhD (with Dr Alan Hudson)
2004	T Mazarkis PhD (with Dr Sue Wilson)
2004	S Argyropoulos MD (Bristol)
2004	J Melichar MD (Bristol)
2004	R Hayward (with Dr Lingford-Hughes)
2003	D Slattery PhD (with Dr Alan Hudson)
2004	G Jackson PhD (with Dr Alan Hudson)
2004	A Kimura PhD (with Dr Alan Hudson)
2004	L Paterson PhD (with Dr Alan Hudson)
2005	N Anderson PhD (with Dr Alan Hudson)
2006	J Man PhD (with Dr Alan Hudson)
2009	M Daglish MD (with Dr Lingford-Hughes)
2008	H Abou Gazaleh PhD (with Dr Alan Hudson)
2009	J Hicks MD (with Dr Sue Wilson)
2010	A Papadopolous PhD (with Professor Hans Ruel)
2009	R Carhart-Harris PhD (with Dr Sue Wilson)
2010	T Williams MD (with Dr Anne Lingford-Hughes)
2012	J Myers (with Dr Anne Lingford-Hughes)
2014	D Quelch PhD (with Dr Christine Parker)
2016	M Nazanin. PhD (with Dr Magdalana Sastre)
2016	K Mendel PhD (with Dr Robin Carhart-Harris)
2016	A Santos Ribeiro PhD (with Dr J McGonigle)

2020	C Timmerman-Slater PhD (with Dr Carhart-Harris)
2020	T Lyons PhD (with Professor Thomas Knopfel)
submitting 2021	Chen-Lai Lan PhD (with Dr Matt Wall and Dr Jim Myers)
submitting 2022	Rayyan Zafar PhD (with Dr David Erritzoe)

Index

Symbols

4-MTA. See *methylamphetamine (4-MTA)*

5-HT, etc. See *serotonin (5-HT)*

A

Act of Supremacy *162*

Advisory Council on the Misuse of
    Drugs (ACMD) *99, 110, 141*

Afghanistan *215*

Africa *94*

agonists *56, 211*

    anti-/contra/inverse agonists *57–66*

agoraphobia *64*

AIDS/HIV *111, 129, 141*

alcohol *23, 91–98, 127, 212, 220*

    Alcoholics Anonymous (AA) *211*

    alcohol tolerance *94*

    binge drinking *95*

    drinks industry *97, 105, 128, 141*

    foetal alcohol syndrome *92*

    mead *94*

    minimum price (Scotland) *95*

    National Institute of Alcohol and Alco-
        holism *66*

    treatment for alcoholism *220*

    UK consumption *95*

    unit pricing *96*

Alexander Mosley Charitable Trust *213,
    220*

    Mosley Foundation *198*

alkyl nitrates. See *poppers*

Allen, Lily *167*

alprazolam *66*

amino acids *29, 82*

amnesia *182*

amphetamine *33, 42, 44, 75, 127, 129*

    methamphetamine (crystal meth) *93,
        106, 134*

amygdala *68, 87, 195*

    enhanced amygdala activation *219*

amyl nitrite *164*

anabolic steroids *127*

anaesthetic *48–50, 57, 165*

anethole. See *aniseed oil*

animal testing *53, 76*

    monkeys *56, 100, 106*

    rats *33, 56*

aniseed oil *102*

anorexia *213*

Anslinger, Harry *152*

antihistamine *74*

anxiety *25, 53–72, 74, 94, 121, 215*

    anxiety research *58*

apology *137*

apomorphine *42*

242

For information about our wide
range of publications putting
justice into words please visit:

www.WatersidePress.co.uk